DUQUESNE STUDIES

Philosophical Series

21

PHENOMENOLOGY AND PHYSICAL SCIENCE

DUQUESNE STUDIES

Philosophical Series

21

PHENOMENOLOGY AND PHYSICAL SCIENCE

An Introduction to the Philosophy of Physical Science

by

Joseph J. Kockelmans, Ph.D.

Duquesne University Press, Pittsburgh, Pa.

Editions E. Nauwelaerts, Louvain

1966

DUQUESNE STUDIES

Philosophical Series

Andrew G. van Melsen, D.Sc., D.Ed., and Henry J. Koren, C.S. Sp. S.T.D., editors

Volume One—*Andrew G. van Melsen*, From Atomos to Atom. Pp. XII and 240. Published also in Dutch, German, Spanish and Italian editions. Available only in Torch book paperback edition.

Volume Two—*Andrew G. van Melsen,* The Philosophy of Nature. Pp. XII and 265. Third edition, fourth impression. Price: paper $3.75, cloth $4.50. Published also in Italian, Dutch and Polish editions.

Volume Three—*P. Henry van Laer,* Philosophico-Scientific Problems. Out of print.

Volume Four—*Cajetan's* The Analogy of Names and The Concept of Being. Pp. X and 93. Second edition. Price: $2.25, cloth.

Volume Five—*Louis de Raeymaeker and others,* Truth and Freedom. Pp. VII and 132. Second impression. Price: $3.00 cloth. Published also in French.

Volume Six—*P. Henry van Laer,* The Philosophy of Science. Part One: Science in General. Pp. XVII and 164. Second edition. Price: cloth $3.75.

Volume Seven—*Stephan Strasser,* The Soul, In Metaphysical and Empirical Psychology. Pp. X and 275. Third impression. Price: cloth $6.00. Published also in German, Dutch and French.

Volume Eight—*Albert Dondeyne,* Contemporary European Thought and Christian Faith. Pp. XI and 211. Second impression. Price: paper $5.00, cloth $5.75. Published also in French.

Library of Congress Catalog Card Number: 66-17126

©1966, by DUQUESNE UNIVERSITY

Volume Nine—*Maxwell J. Charlesworth*, PHILOSOPHY AND LINGUISTIC ANALYSIS. Pp. XIII and 234. Second impression. Price: paper $4.75, cloth $5.50.

Volume Ten—*Remy C. Kwant*, PHILOSOPHY OF LABOR. Pp. XI and 163. Price: paper $4.50, cloth $5.25. Italian and Spanish editions in preparation.

Volume Eleven—*Remy C. Kwant*, ENCOUNTER. Pp. VIII and 85. Second impression. Price: cloth $3.25. Published also in Dutch.

Volume Twelve—*William A. Luijpen*, EXISTENTIAL PHENOMENOLOGY. Pp. XIII and 355. Fourth impression. Price: cloth $6.25. Published also in Dutch. German and Spanish editions in preparation.

Volume Thirteen—*Andrew G. van Melsen*, SCIENCE AND TECHNOLOGY. Pp. X and 373. Price: paper $6.20, cloth $6.95. Published also in Dutch and German.

Volume Fourteen—*P. Henry van Laer*, PHILOSOPHY OF SCIENCE. PART TWO: A STUDY OF THE DIVISION AND NATURE OF VARIOUS GROUPS OF SCIENCES. Pp. XIII and 342. Price: paper $5.75, cloth, $6.50.

Volume Fifteen—*Remy C. Kwant*, THE PHENOMENOLOGICAL PHILOSOPHY OF MERLEAU-PONTY. Pp. IX and 257. Price: paper $4.50, cloth $5.25.

Volume Sixteen—*John A. Peters*, METAPHYSICS: A SYSTEMATIC SURVEY. Pp. XVIII and 529. Price: paper $9.00, cloth $9.75.

Volume Seventeen—*William A. Luijpen*, PHENOMENOLOGY AND ATHEISM. Pp. XIV and 342. Price: paper $5.75, cloth $6.50.

Volume Eighteen—*Martin G. Plattel*, SOCIAL PHILOSOPHY. Pp. XI and 346. Price: paper $7.20, cloth $7.95. Published also in Dutch and German.

Volume Nineteen—*Andrew G. van Melsen*, EVOLUTION AND PHILOSOPHY. Pp. 208. Price: paper $4.75, cloth $5.50.

Volume Twenty—*Remy C. Kwant*, FROM PHENOMENOLOGY TO METAPHYSICS. Pp. 247. Price: paper $7.20, cloth $7.95.

Volume Twenty-One—*Joseph J. Kockelmans*, PHENOMENOLOGY AND PHYSICAL SCIENCE. Pp. 208. Price: paper $6.20, cloth $6.95.

In preparation
William A. Luijpen, PHENOMENOLOGY OF NATURAL LAW

Dedicated to Prof. Dr. Adrian D. Fokker

in admiration and friendship

PREFACE

In the sixteenth century an ever-widening chasm began to develop between philosophy and the sciences of nature. When, subsequently, other empirical sciences arose, they sought contact with the sciences of nature rather than with philosophy. As a consequence, the chasm became even wider and more profound. In spite of all the efforts of traditional philosophy to stop this fatal development, philosophy and the sciences continued to grow farther apart.

Positivism, which arose in the middle of the nineteenth century, thought that all difficulties could be solved by doubting the possibility of an autonomous philosophy and by denying to philosophy, in the traditional sense of the term, the right to existence. In its view, the sole task of philosophy is to co-ordinate the results achieved by the various sciences. Most philosophers, however, have obstinately continued to resist the positivistic view and profess to see more in philosophy than a synthesis of the results attained by the various sciences. Yet one cannot deny that in their discussions and defenses these philosophers have often committed serious mistakes.

At present the dispute has lost most of its acrimonious character. Many of those who pursue the various sciences have come to realize the limitations proper to the object of their pursuit and the restricted possibilities which the methods of their science permit. Thus the time seems to have come to raise once again the question of the relationship between philosophy and the sciences. It appears to us that the theory of science proper to phenomenological philosophy contains principles and insights which supply us with a key to solve the problems in question, to the satisfaction of both philosophy and science.

Accordingly, in this book we intend to explain the proper character of physical science in the light of phenomenological philosophy. We will do this by an analytic consideration and description of the theoretical attitude assumed by the physicist and of the intentional correlate which he tries to attain by way of this theoretical attitude. To justify our procedure to some extent, we will start with a discussion of those aspects

7

of phenomenology that are indispensable to a good understanding of the purpose pursued by this book.

It is, of course, not our intention to claim that this work is complete or definitive. We consider it merely a provisional attempt to pursue a new line of philosophical reflection. It is our hope that it may lead to a discussion in which the scientists themselves will play a major role. Such a discussion could serve not only to eliminate mistakes made in this book but also to develop the sound ideas that, I hope, are not entirely lacking to it.

A word of thanks is due to Dr. Adrian D. Fokker, Professor of Physical Science (Emeritus) at the University of Leyden, and to Dr. Remy C. Kwant, Professor of Philosophy at the University of Utrecht. They have read major portions of the manuscript with the greatest care. Many of their valuable suggestions have been gratefully incorporated into the text.

Joseph J. Kockelmans

In the American edition of this book the intentional analysis of physical science (Part Two) has been restricted to a consideration of the theory of relativity. This theory is sufficiently general to throw light on the proper character of the physicist's activity and on nature as the correlate of his attitude toward reality.

To make a distinction between *Sein* and *Seiendes* without having recourse to a neologism such as essent, we have translated *Sein* by *being* and *Seiendes* by *be-ing*.

Our thanks are due to the author for his remarks and suggestions regarding the translation of this work, and to Mrs. Elizabeth Connolly for her careful revision of the finished manuscript.

Duquesne University   Henry J. Koren, C.S.Sp.
Pittsburgh, Pa.

TABLE OF CONTENTS

PREFACE 7

CHAPTER ONE—INTRODUCTION

1. Some Philosophical Ideas 13
2. The Aim Pursued in this Book 18
3. The Logic of the Physical Sciences 19

PART ONE
PHILOSOPHY AND SCIENCE ACCORDING TO THE STANDPOINT OF PHENOMENOLOGY

Introductory Remarks 29

CHAPTER TWO—PHENOMENOLOGY AS METHOD

1. Philosophy as a Rigorous Science 30
2. Intentional and Constitutive Analyses 40

CHAPTER THREE—INTENTIONALITY AND EXISTENCE

1. The Question of Being—*Dasein* 49
2. Existence as the Central Reference Point of Existential
   Phenomenology 51
3. Materialism, Spiritualism, and Existential Phenomenology . . 54
4. Subjectivity and Existence 59
5. Transcendence and Project—Freedom 64

CHAPTER FOUR—PHILOSOPHY AND SCIENCE

1. Historical Considerations of the Theory of Science 70
2. Scientism 72
3. Scientism and Psychology 76
4. The Crisis of the Scientistic View 78
5. Phenomenology and Scientism 81

6. The Essential Distinction Between Science and Philosophy . . 85
7. Scientific Objectivation 87

PART TWO
INTENTIONAL ANALYSIS OF A CONTEMPORARY PHYSICAL THEORY: THE THEORY OF RELATIVITY

Introductory Remarks 95

CHAPTER FIVE—A FEW HIGHLIGHTS IN THE HISTORY OF THE THEORY OF RELATIVITY

1. The Philosophers' Distrust of Einstein's Theory 98
2. From Classical Mechanics to Relativity 103

CHAPTER SIX—PHYSICAL MAGNITUDES—MEASUREMENTS

1. The Aim of the Theory of Relativity 111
2. The Measurement of Physical Magnitudes 112
3. Demands to be Met by the Definition of a Physical Quantity . 116
4. The Classical Idea Concerning the Measurements of Length
   and Time 117

CHAPTER SEVEN—EINSTEIN'S CRITIQUE OF THE CLASSICAL IDEAS OF MEASURING SPACE AND TIME

1. The Problems: Isochronism and Synchronism 120
2. Isochronism According to Classical Physics 121
3. The Standpoint of Classical Physics with Respect to
   Synchronism 125

CHAPTER EIGHT—EINSTEIN'S IDEAS CONCERNING SPACE AND TIME

1. The Starting Point of the Theory of Relativity 128
2. Einstein's Idea of the Measurement of Length 130
3. Einstein's Definition of Simultaneity 133
4. The Measurement of Time. Relativity of Space and Time. . 135
5. The Doctrine of Absolute Relations 138

CHAPTER NINE—Nature As the Intentional Correlate of Physical Science, Viewed from the Theory of Relativity

1. The Intentional Correlate of Physical Science 151
2. The Intentional Correlate of the Physical Attitude in the Theory of Relativity 153
3. Being and Becoming 157

PART THREE
Physical Science: Its Nature and Relation to Philosophy

Introductory Remarks 161

CHAPTER TEN—The Proper Character of Physical Science

1. The World of the Physicist 163
2. Physical Science and Technology 170

CHAPTER ELEVEN—Physical Science and Philosophy

1. Collaboration of Science and Philosophy 176
2. The Concrete Road from Physical Science to Philosophy . . 181

BIBLIOGRAPHY 185

INDEX OF NAMES 199

INDEX OF SUBJECT MATTER 201

CHAPTER ONE

INTRODUCTION

1. Some Philosophical Ideas

Intentionality. One of the most important topics of contemporary thought centers around the idea of intentionality proposed by phenomenological philosophy. The first point to strike anyone who makes a study of this idea is the fact that phenomenological philosophy views intentionality not merely as a certain relationship between knowing and the object known, but also and primarily as a relationship of being between man and the world.[1] We intend to speak extensively about this point in the second chapter and will indicate there the reasons for this view. If it is permitted to anticipate on what will be said there, we may say that the expression "intentionality," in its primordial sense, indicates that man is being-in-the-world.[2] From the standpoint of this view concerning intentionality, the essence of man lies in his existence, in his openness to the world.[3] For this reason man's essence is sometimes described as openness and freedom.

This freedom, however, should not be conceived as absolute, for the existence through which man is in-and-to-the-world can become involved in the world only from a given physical, historical, and social situation and this situation always co-determines man's attitude toward the world.[4] In other words, the freedom which man is, is always permeated with facticity which, as the subject's initial situation, has to be transcended in and through freedom. For this reason man is a "potentiality for being" (*Sein-können*)[5] which constantly discovers itself as already-situated and, as such, knows that, despite all its

---

[1] Maurice Merleau-Ponty, *Sens et Non-sens,* Paris, 1948, pp. 142-144; M. Heidegger, *Sein und Zeit,* Tübingen, 1953, p. 61 (English ed., p. 88).
[2] Heidegger, *op. cit.,* p. 53 (English ed., p. 78); Merleau-Ponty, *Phenomenology of Perception,* New York, 1962, p. 121, footnote 5.
[3] Heidegger, *op. cit.,* p. 42 (English ed., p. 67).
[4] Merleau-Ponty, *Sens et Non-Sens,* p. 143.
[5] Heidegger, *op. cit.,* p. 143 (English ed., p. 183).

possibilities, it is limited in its actual projects.[6]   Man is essentially a "possibility of situations."[7]

Relationship Between Philosophical and Pre-philosophical Thinking. Not only man's being but every aspect of his existence and all his actions are marked by the fact that they originate in a situation.   This statement applies also to man's knowledge and science.   All reflection occurs in a situation.   The world and our own being never become problems to us unless we are already familiar with them, at least in a superficial and provisional fashion.   We know already that we are in the world and acquainted with the things of the world when we begin to wonder about the world.   Prior to any philosophy, we live in an understanding of the world.   The wealth contained in this understanding lies still hidden behind its apparent obviousness; but, nonetheless, this primordial understanding of the world determines and illuminates our human existence. Thus, when philosophy begins its reflection, it is always preceded by man's understanding of his own life and of the world.

This relationship between philosophy and pre-philosophical life is characterized by two aspects.   On the one hand, pre-philosophical life is the root and foundation of philosophy, but on the other, there is great danger that the "obvious" character of pre-philosophical understanding will constantly jeopardize the life of philosophy.

Philosophy is the explicitation of our pre-philosophical living in and with the world; it discloses the truths implicitly contained in this life.   It transposes our original understanding of the world and of ourselves into philosophical concepts.   It leads us to a higher degree of truth but does not essentially change our primordial understanding of being, provided our explicitations and explanations remain within the confines imposed by what is actually given in our original being-to-the-world.

It is possible to take a more radical view of the relationship between philosophy and pre-philosophical life.   Philosophy is not only, and not even primarily, a conceptual development of previous everyday knowledge concerning the world and man himself, but is first of all the destruction of this knowledge.   Let us clarify this statement in a few words.

When we raise philosophical problems, we but rarely do not know enough.   Usually we know too much.   For, when we begin to philosophize, we drift around in a sea of meanings, views, vague ideas

---

[6] Merleau-Ponty, *Phenomenology of Perception,* p. 453.

[7] Merleau-Ponty, *ibid.,* p. 407.

and conceptions which we have acquired in numerous ways and which, later, nearly always appear to be prejudices. Our human existence in its original understanding of the world and of itself is fettered by the almost inescapable obviousness proper to the views unquestioningly accepted by everyone. Thus, the asking of philosophical questions and replying to them have, as their first task, to fight against the dangerous current of all this unquestioned obviousness of everyday life.

We do not mean to say that one can simply rid oneself of these unquestioned prejudices and make a fresh start. One does not escape from the dominion of unquestioned obviousness by a simple heroic resolution or by assigning names to these prejudices, for they often control our thought without being discovered. For this reason the procedure which phenomenology calls "phenomenological reduction" is indispensable. This absolutely necessary procedure, which is at the same time extremely difficult, presents itself at first as the destruction of our natural, naive certainties regarding the world and ourselves.[8]

The Historical Character of Philosophical Thinking. As we have said, all philosophical reflection begins in a situation and this situation is, in part, determined by our pre-philosophical life. Other factors, however, also play a role in this situation. One of these must be mentioned here. Our human life in the world is already determined by a given situation in this sense also that it is essentially the taking-up of a history. Our existence is not only openness to the world but also openness to the future on the basis of a particular given past. This past, on the basis of which we live, is not limited to our own personal history but encompasses, also, the past of all those in whose life we somehow share and, ultimately, even the past of all mankind. Every human activity bears the seal of this determination by a historical situation. Thus, even our most personal philosophical reflection always remains a thinking within the limits of a philosophical tradition, because the problems and methods of our thinking are to some extent dependent on a philosophical tradition. In our philosophical reflection we always inherit a certain past, even when we do not pay attention to it and even if we desire to rid ourselves of the past.

This relationship between our own philosophy and the philosophical life of the past also has two aspects. On the one hand, the philosophical tradition is an indispensable source for our own contemporary thinking,

---

[8] Concerning this matter see also E. Fink, *Zur ontologischen Frühgeschichte von Raum—Zeit—Bewegung,* Den Haag, 1957, pp. 14–21.

but on the other, this indispensable good creates a great danger that our own reflection will never reach the level on which genuine and authentic philosophizing can be attained.

Accordingly, our philosophical thinking inevitably begins in a given situation that is explicitly or implicitly determined by the history of philosophy. Every systematic reflection in the realm of philosophy is essentially a historical reflection. Every systematic philosophical problem either implies or is a historical problem. The philosophical past is never completely lost to us, for it helps us to penetrate into the present and enriches our presence in being. The genuinely great ideas of a major philosopher never vanish into the shades of a past that is lost forever, even though it is true that these ideas will never live again save through our own thinking. But if the thinking of past ages rises to new life in us, then by this very fact we transcend the narrow boundaries of our own finite mind. Without the great thinkers of the past our sensitivity for the mystery of being that permeates and supports us would not be what it is now.

It is impossible, of course, for anyone to dominate fully the entire history of philosophy. A single man does not have the time to read, evaluate and live every thought of hundreds of important philosophers. Moreover, with respect to the past, we can understand only that which somehow appeals to us because it is related to our own thought. As Hegel expresses it, "The living spirit which dwells in a philosophy demands, in order to reveal itself, to be born from a kindred spirit."[9] For this reason our taking-up of the philosophical past will always, and of necessity, be limited and, consequently, imply a choice. This necessity to make a choice contains a first element of danger, for the limitation of our own mind may make this choice needlessly one-sided and narrow.

The necessary bond with a philosophical tradition, however, contains a second and greater danger. This danger is so great that for many it has led to the death of authentic thinking. While it is true that our life and thinking consist essentially in the taking-up of a history, our entry into history, nonetheless, demands that we remain ourselves even though we orient our understanding of being through the thinking of past philosophers and nourish ourselves on their thought. Therefore, we must learn to place ourselves, as it were, at a distance from the thinking of the past, and thus permit the past to appear to us as it really was.

---

[9] Hegel, *Differenz des Fichtischen und Schellingschen System der Philosophie*, quoted by E. Fink, *op. cit.*, pp. 29-30.

Only then will we be able to ask how this thinking can be made actual again, how we can take it up by determining our attitude toward it.

Accordingly, when we say that our philosophical thinking is connected with a philosophical tradition, we want to convey the idea that our contemporary thinking is essentially historical, that, as today's thought, it is of necessity rooted in the past. All authentic human thinking is necessarily rooted in a historical situation. One who denies this situated character either does not think in an authentically human fashion or does not understand his own thought.

This assertion, however, should be properly understood. It would be wrong to assume that one could first take part in contemporary thinking and only then raise the question: How can modern thinking, *post factum,* be located and assigned a basis in this or that philosophical tradition? Secondly, it would not be right to ask how the thinking of the past, taken up again by me, has to adapt itself to contemporary thinking. It seems to us that either of these questions attempts to isolate aspects which are essentially connected. Between our contemporary thinking and the philosophical thought of the past there exist essentially a dialectic relationship. One who attempts to separate the two retains only an abstraction. All authentic philosophical thought is necessarily a thinking in the present, but as thinking-in-the-present it is essentially a taking-up of a philosophical tradition. It is hardly necessary to add that these genetic connections are rarely explicit in our consciousness.

It is important to keep in mind that this connection with a history of thought cannot consist in passively rethinking certain philosophical insights. Neither is it a development and perfecting of elements that remained unfinished in the great thinkers of the past. On the contrary, the taking-up of a philosophical tradition lies in assuming once more an authentically philosophical attitude of mind and, a renewed reflection on the age-old problems. With respect to the last-named point, it is not so much a question of saying again in different words what has been said in the past, or even primarily of trying to find entirely new solutions to these problems. The point of primary importance is that we ourselves take up again these age-old problems from the standpoint of a central reference point, a fundamental intuition.[10]

---

[10] Cf. Merleau-Ponty, *Sens et Non-Sens,* pp. 165–196; A. de Waelhens, *Une philosophie de l'ambiguïté. L'existentialisme de Maurice Merleau-Ponty,* Louvain, 1951, pp. 331-365; A. Dondeyne, *Contemporary European Thought and Christian Faith,* Pittsburgh, 2nd impr., 1963, pp. 47–53; "L'historicité dans la philosophie contemporaine," *Revue philosophique de Louvain,* vol. 54 (1956), pp. 5-25 and 456-477; Fink, *op. cit.,* pp. 27-39.

2. The Aim Pursued in this Book

In the following pages we intend, in connection with the history of the sciences, to reflect on the old problem of the relationship between philosophy and the physical sciences in the light of the fundamental intuition which contemporary thought has formulated concerning the original relationship between man and the world. Since the time of Descartes, and especially since the end of the nineteenth century and its critique of the sciences, much has been written about the philosophy of physical science. Against the background of the most divergent philosophical trends, efforts have been made to formulate and solve the relevant problems. On the basis of our remarks concerning the historicity of human thought, stressed by existential phenomenology, one could perhaps expect that we would begin by situating our view of the philosophy of physical science in reference to other views. However, we must renounce the attempt to do so since it would lead us beyond the scope of this book. Nevertheless, we will occasionally have an opportunity to make a few remarks regarding this matter. Furthermore, we will have to explain certain points concerning the logic of the physical sciences in order to prevent serious misunderstandings.

If we limit ourselves to the philosophy of physical science in the strict sense of the term, we may say in general that the books and articles devoted to this subject contain many valuable ideas. But, nonetheless, the philosophical backgrounds from which these ideas have risen often appear to be unacceptable to us. For this reason we first want to describe briefly, but as clearly as possible, the fundamental intuition of existential phenomenology and then make explicit those elements in it that are of importance for the remainder of this study.

In our description and analysis of this fundamental intuition we will begin with a brief historical study of Husserl's conception of phenomenology. We will see that Husserl at first viewed phenomenology as a method of philosophy. The core and root of this method is constituted by an entirely new conception of intentionality. However, no radical foundation can be assigned to Husserl's original concept of intentionality. Using his later distinction between the "intentionality of a simple and determined act" (*Aktintentionalität*) and the "functioning intentionality itself" (*fungierende Intentionalität*)[11] we will then proceed to that

---

[11] For the distinction between *Aktintentionalität* and *fungierende Intentionalität* in Husserl's work, see G. Brand, *Welt, Ich und Zeit,* Den Haag, 1955, pp. 22–25.

idea of intentionality which has become the central intuition of contemporary existential phenomenology.

In our study of intentionality we will devote special attention to the so-called "intentional analysis." For, to a certain extent this analysis is the phenomenological method *par excellence;* moreover, in the remainder of this book this analysis, we hope, will provide us with the appropriate methodic means for the concrete analyses to be made of one of the most important contemporary theories of physical science, viz., the theory of relativity (Part Two). We will close our discussion of phenomenology with a consideration of the proper relationship existing between phenomenological philosophy and the sciences. The result attained by these "epistemological investigations" will provide us with the background against which we can, on the basis of the above-mentioned analyses, form a judgment regarding the proper nature of contemporary physical science and its relationship to philosophy (Part Three).

As we have said, in the second part of this study we will investigate the theory of relativity by means of the intentional analysis proper to phenomenology. A few important aspects of this theory will be analytically described in order to arrive at an insight into the proper intentional correlate of physical science, to the extent that this correlate reveals itself to us in this theory.

3. *The Logic of the Physical Sciences*

As we have indicated above, we intend to preface the main topic of this book with a few remarks about the logic of the physical sciences because it is extremely important to situate very clearly, with respect to the conceptions proposed by logicians, what we are going to say philosophically about the physical sciences. What logic teaches about physical theories as deductive systems and about the interpretation of these theories through so-called "semantic analyses" appears to be very important for anyone who wants to discern the *physical* meaning of these theories. Nevertheless, in our opinion, logic is unable to arrive at an authentically *philosophical* interpretation of physical theories. Let us clarify these assertions.

Deductive Theory and Physical Reality. It has almost become commonplace to state that physical science proceeds, more or less explicitly, from general hypotheses, from which, by means of logic and mathematics, one can deduce certain consequences that can be tested through observation and experiments for their true value with respect to the events of nature. Nevertheless, the implications contained in this view of physical science are, logically speaking, not at all trivial. Physical science is not satisfied with observing physical facts and formulating them in general statements, but endeavors to deduce these general statements of the lower order from more general hypotheses on a higher level and assemble them in a deductive system. The building of such a system requires complex mathematical methods, and a correct understanding of the proper meaning of the system demands accurate logical analyses.

Moreover, the most general hypotheses of physical science often contain concepts and notions which do not seem to refer to immediately observable properties of physical entities but can be connected with such properties only by means of rather complex logical relationships. Thus the question arises spontaneously as to what value such a deductive theory has with respect to physical reality. If physical reality is in the way described by the deductive theory, then the question must be asked why this theory contains concepts and notions that cannot be immediately connected with directly observable facts, conditions, and events. And if physical reality is different from what the theorical description says, then the question is what value the theory has in reference to reality.[12]

Syntactic Analyses and Semantic Analyses. Accordingly, the logic of the physical sciences contains two different kinds of considerations. There are syntactic analyses, which explain the formal-logical structure of the deductive system by describing the system of symbols, rules for the formation of sentences and definitions, axioms, and rules of inference. There are also semantic analyses, which endeavor to establish a connection between the combinations of symbols in the purely formal calculus and the domain of physical entities. In a physical theory, moreover, it is generally possible to distinguish two elements in the formal calculus, viz., the specific physical deductive system and a logico-mathematical basic calculus without which it would not be possible to prove any proposition of the system or to justify any deduction from it.[13]

With respect to the construction of any particular physical theory, one could start with the construction of a physical calculus and subsequently

---

[12] R. Braithwaite, *Scientific Explanation,* Cambridge, 1959, pp. ix-x.

[13] E. Beth, *Wijsbegeerte der wiskunde,* Antwerpen, 1948, p. 167; R. Carnap, "Foundations of Logic and Mathematics," *International Encyclopedia of Unified Science,* Vol. I, no. 3, Chicago, 1957, pp. 6-38; A. Tarski, *Introduction to Logic,* New York, 1951, pp. 117-130.

determine in an explicit fashion how this calculus is to be interpreted through semantic rules. In that case, on the basis of the logico-mathematical basic calculus and of the axioms proper to the physical theory in question, these rules have to establish a bridge between the syntactical system that has been constructed and the class of bodies, motions and events for which the system has been devised. It is only through this descriptive interpretation given in the semantic rules that the sentences of the calculus become genuine statements about nature and, consequently, laws of nature subject to experimental verification.

Generally speaking, the construction of the calculi and the making of the deductions are the work of the theorist. The duty of the experimenter, on the other hand, is to find the descriptive interpretation of these calculi and then to check the interpreted system through experiments in its various theorems in order to determine its actual truth. Superficially considered, the work of the theorist appears to be a kind of mathematics. While, in general, this mathematical character cannot be denied, it is oriented, nonetheless, to physical science by way of its subsequent semantic interpretation. For this reason there exists an essential difference between a mathematical and a physical theorem. This difference lies in the entirely different concept of truth that is implicitly presupposed in the two types of theorems because of the semantic rules which follow later in an explicit fashion. A mathematical theorem possesses only logical truth, but the truth of a physical theorem depends also on the properties of the entities which are intended by the symbols of the formal system.[14]

The question may be asked where, abstractly speaking, the descriptive interpretation of the physical calculi can best begin if a physical theory is devised on the basis of such a calculus. One could reply that, with the aid of suitable semantic rules, one should at once connect a descriptive interpretation with the very axioms proper to the physical theory. As a matter of fact, physical science used to proceed in this fashion for centuries. With respect to the most modern theories, however, an entirely different procedure is followed. Here one begins by formulating very general axioms without attaching any physical meaning to them. Next, the necessary rules of inference are laid down and by means of these rules new theorems are deduced from the axioms. Only after this,

---

[14] Carnap, *op. cit.*, pp. 56 f.

are certain theorems of the calculus connected with physical entities through well-chosen semantic rules.[15]

Accordingly, in modern physical science the semantic rules do not immediately refer to the original terms of the system but circumscribe the physical meaning of terms that appear in the theory only after a long series of deductions. From the highest possible abstraction modern physical science descends to ever lower degrees of abstraction in order to anchor explicitly, through its semantic rules, only the last step on the firm basis of observable facts. An unavoidable consequence of this is that a modern physical calculus can no longer be verified in its axioms or even in all its theorems. Verification of the calculus is made by deducing concrete predictions from the formal system through semantic rules. If these predictions are confirmed by perceived phenomena, we are justified in claiming that in this particular interpretation the physical calculus is valid.[16]

Parts of Any Physical Theory. In any physical theory, therefore, three clearly distinct parts can be indicated. First of all, any physical theory contains certain fundamental equations. For instance, in classical mechanics we find Newton's equations of motion and in the theory of electromagnetic phenomena we find Maxwell's electromagnetic field equations. These equations use terms such as "coordinate," "time" and "force." Propositions built with such terms cannot be verified immediately through observation and experimentation. Also the logical consistency of these equations is not immediately verifiable. One could call these equations the calculus of the domain "physics."

In addition to this calculus, we must distinguish in every physical theory a second calculus, which may be conceived as the logical foundation of the first. This second calculus teaches us the transformations that may be applied to the first equations without changing their nature. It is only by means of this logico-mathematical basic calculus that the consistency of the first calculus can be demonstrated.

However, the system of these physical equations and logico-mathematical rules and laws does not yet constitute a physical theory, it is not yet an orderly system of physical laws. Rules and statements have to be added which define the physical meaning of the terms "distance," "time," "moment," "simultaneity," "force," "mass," "field," etc. This third

---

[15] Carnap, *ibid.,* p. 64.

[16] Carnap, *ibid.,* pp. 60-64; cf. also A. Einstein, "On the Method of Theoretical Physics," *Philosophy of Science,* vol. 1 (1934), pp. 163-169.

essential part of a physical theory is called the semantic system of the theory in question. It contains such terms as "one yard long," "warm water," "a wooden rod," and "yellow light." These terms are to be understood in the customary sense of everyday usage. Without this appeal to ordinary language it would not be possible to make use of the scientific language of physical science. Only through the semantic rules is it possible to conceive the equations of physical theories as laws of nature which can be verified through experiments.[17]

The Importance of the Semantic Rules. Thus we see that the semantic rules establish a bridge between the theoretical deductive system of the physical theories and physical reality. That which is found in the equations of the physical theory, its logical and mathematical entities and the greater complexes which the calculus builds from these entities, considered in themselves, do not possess more than a purely formal or logical truth. However, these entities can easily be conceived as constant or variable magnitudes to which the semantic rules will assign a physical meaning. If this is true, then it should be evident that the semantic rules of a physical theory most appropriately assume the form of rules describing certain physical operations, such as counting and measuring, in such a way that we arrive at pointer readings that can be connected with the variables of the equations.

Long before logic had arrived at this idea, Bridgman had discovered the necessity and character of these rules. He called them, not without justification, "operational definitions." If we know these rules, we also know the "operational meaning" of a term used in the physical argument. According to Bridgman, Newton's equations of motion alone do not constitute his theory of motion, but this theory is constituted by these equations together with the operational meaning determined by the operational definitions in question. If the equations are taken in themselves, there is no possibility of checking whether, physically speaking, they are valid or true. "We can check only whether a *system* of equations *plus* the operational definitions is confirmed by a certain experiment or not." Although, as we will see, Bridgman's view is correct, it seems better to speak with modern logic about basic equations, a logico-mathematical calculus, and semantic rules.[18]

---

[17] Ph. Frank, "Foundations of Physics," *International Encyclopedia of Unified Science*, Vol. I, no. 7, pp. 3 f.

[18] Frank, *ibid.*, pp. 4 f.; P. Bridgman, *Logic of Modern Physics*, New York, 1927.

The Necessity of Reflection on the Semantic Rules.   There is still another way in which one can clarify the value and importance of the operational definitions or semantic rules.   In the past few centuries the empirical sciences of nature were extremely successful, while the other empirical sciences and also philosophy encountered the greatest difficulties. This situation led several thinkers to the idea that these other sciences could be brought to bloom by applying to them the method of physical science.   This idea continues to find support even in our own twentieth century.   In the past few decades many have tried to enrich the non-physical sciences by applying to them ideas derived from the theories of relativity and quantum mechanics.

Let us quote a few examples.   Biologists have appealed to quantum mechanics to settle the age-old issue between the mechanistic and vitalistic views of life in favor of vitalism.   The same theory exercises a similar influence in medical science.   In sociology and economics it was considered possible to borrow arguments from contemporary physical science to oppose the materialistic and mechanistic views of society defended by Marxism.   Psychology, philosophy and even theology occasionally show traces of similar efforts.   By "applying" certain methodic ideas and attained results of the physical sciences, some of these other sciences sometimes managed to achieve sensational successes. Efforts were made to integrate the symbols and equations of physical science into the domains of the other sciences without paying attention to the semantic rules which connect these symbols and equations with physical reality.   The operational definitions of the physical sciences were simply replaced by the semantic rules proper to the various other sciences.   No one appeared to realize that this procedure was bound to lead to hopeless confusion.

A few examples may serve to illustrate the point.   Understood in its operational meaning, the statement of the theory of relativity, "length is relative," means that certain measuring operations will lead to different results even though one would at first have expected the same measurements.   If, however, that statement is transferred to the domains of sociology or psychology without the above-described operational meaning, the term "relative" will easily be given the sense which it has had for centuries in philosophy and these sciences.   Thus, the term will readily lead to the conclusion that all our knowledge is "subjective," historically determined, and ethnically conditioned.   If, on the other hand, the term "relative," together with the operational definition it has in the theory of relativity, is transferred to the domain of the other sciences, then there is no danger that anyone will conclude that our knowledge in these fields is "subjective" or inevitably affected by a certain agnosticism.

When quantum mechanics, to give another example, argues that the concepts of classical mechanics may not be applied to processes within the atom, its meaning is that the symbols of Newtonian mechanics have no accurately determined operational meaning in the domain of these intra-atomic processes. But, as we have mentioned, among biologists there existed an old controversy between mechanistic and vitalistic views of life. The vitalists claimed that the concepts of mechanics cannot be applied to living beings, because life is something autonomous and spontaneous and develops beyond the control of deterministic forces. When the theory of quantum mechanics had been formulated, some vitalists thought that this theory supported their view. For, as was often claimed, quantum mechanics showed that determinism and causality were meaningless with respect to intra-atomic entities. If, however, the symbols of quantum mechanics are taken together with their operational meaning, they evidently have no reference to spontaneity, autonomy, and evolution in the sense in which these concepts are used in biology. Understood in terms of biological language, contemporary physical science is neither less nor more "mechanistic" than the old physical science. If the physical symbols are constantly taken together with their operational meaning, they do not give rise to any conclusion which would be directly relevant to biology.[19]

Physical Science and Philosophy. Observing such confusions, many physicists thought that physical science should withdraw and isolate itself from philosophy and the other sciences. Obviously, however, such a procedure does not remove the danger and, moreover, such an isolation-ism is wrong in principle. Something more positive has to be done and this, in our opinion, consists in placing greater emphasis on the proper meaning of the semantic rules and in asking, whenever there is a question of concretely applying the methodic means and the theories of physical science to other domains of knowledge, whether or not the passage to the other domain is licit in the light of the relevant semantic rules.[20]

From all this it should be clear that the semantic analyses are very important to determine exactly the *physical* sense of the physical theories.

---

[19] Frank, *op. cit.*, pp. 72-75.
[20] Frank, *ibid.*, p. 75.

Yet care should be taken not to exaggerate the value of these analyses. There are logicians who claim that the logical considerations in question can solve all the pertinent real problems, so that philosophy cannot contribute anything at all. A few do not even hesitate to reject completely philosophy in the traditional sense of the term.

The large majority of thinkers, however, belonging to other philosophical trends readily agree that logical considerations in the above-indicated sense are very fruitful and extremely important, but refuse to admit that such considerations are able to say the last word concerning the theories of physical science. Outside the positivistic fold there is hardly a philosopher who does not claim that the theories of positive science and all their accompanying logical studies can find their ultimate foundation only in philosophy. The reason is that any positive scientific theory contains presuppositions which demand a *radical* foundation and explanation and can obtain them only from philosophy.

These philosophers, moreover, agree that any positive scientific theory expresses something about reality and, therefore, may have value for philosophy itself. With respect to this point, while it may be evident that a solid study of semantics can make exceedingly important contributions, it is equally evident that semantic analyses alone cannot settle the whole issue. The core of the entire problem lies in the fact that operational definitions and semantic rules want to establish a bridge between physical calculus and "reality." All their replies, however, do not say anything radical and definitive as long as one cannot indicate what is meant here by the term "reality." When there is question of the being of things, we are in the realm that for centuries has been known as philosophy. It is for this reason that such problems can receive a radical explanation only in a philosophical study.

PART ONE

PHILOSOPHY AND SCIENCE
ACCORDING TO THE STANDPOINT
OF PHENOMENOLOGY

Introductory Remarks

In this part we want to discuss a few important problems concerning the proper character of philosophy and of the positive sciences, then attempt to determine their mutual relationships. The question of what the proper character of physical science is and the problem of its relationship to philosophy will be considered in the second and third part.

As we have indicated, with respect to the questions pertaining to the theory of science to be studied here, we will take the standpoint of existential phenomenology. Whether this existential phenomenology is essentially in harmony with what Edmund Husserl had in mind or deviates from it is an issue that need not concern us here.[1]

To the best of our knowledge, phenomenological literature does not yet contain any developed theory of science.[2] True, in the writings of Husserl, Heidegger and Merleau-Ponty there are isolated valuable remarks and brief passages, yet they rarely go beyond the fragmentary stage. For this reason we want to develop here the major lines of a phenomenological theory of science, based on ideas contained in Husserl's, Heidegger's, and Merleau-Ponty's occasional remarks. In developing these ideas, we will as closely as possible follow the excellent commentaries of Alphonse de Waelhens, Albert Dondeyne, Frederick Buytendijk, Remy Kwant, and William Luijpen. Thus, it should be evident that we do not intend to attribute an originality or a definitive character to the study presented here. Our aim is mainly to raise a few problems that are of great importance for the philosophy of science in order to prepare the way for the issues to be raised in the other two parts of this book.

As is well-known, Husserl at first presented his phenomenology as a method only, but in the course of time this method revealed itself more and more as implying a whole philosophy. Nonetheless, it remains true that one can continue to speak of phenomenology in the narrower sense as a method for the building of a philosophy. We will speak here, first, about this method according to Husserl's mind; next, we will briefly indicate the interpretation given to it by Heidegger and Merleau-Ponty, paying special attention to the motives that have led them to their interpretation. Only then will we direct our inquiry to the problems pertaining to the theory of science in the strict sense.

---

[1] Cf. Kockelmans, "Realisme—Idealisme en Husserls Phaenomenologie," *Tijdschrift voor Philosophie,* vol. 20 (1958), pp. 395-442 (see especially pp. 430-441.

[2] A first attempt in this direction may be found in R. Kwant, "Het phenomenologisch wetenschapsideaal," *Tijdschrift voor Zielkunde en Opvoedingsleer,* vol. 41 (1955), pp. 2-43.

CHAPTER TWO

PHENOMENOLOGY AS METHOD

1. Philosophy as a Rigorous Science

Hegel's Phenomenology. Anyone familiar with the situation knows that as soon as he uses the term "phenomenology" he enters a sphere of ambiguity. The term was used as early as 1765 in philosophical writings, and Kant occasionally had recourse to it also. Nevertheless, it was only with Hegel that a well-defined technical meaning became attached to it.[3] For Hegel phenomenology was not knowledge of the Absolute-in-and-for-itself, in the spirit of Fichte or Schelling, but in his *Phenomenology of Mind* he wanted solely to consider knowing as it appears to consciousness. In this book Hegel wanted to ascend from this self-criticizing phenomenal knowing to the knowledge of the Absolute, which itself must be called an absolute knowing. Thus, phenomenology for Hegel is the science describing the development which natural phenomenal consciousness undergoes by way of science and philosophy toward the absolute knowing of the Absolute.[4] The object of his investigations, then, was phenomenal knowing.[5]

Although this knowing cannot be considered to be the science *par excellence,* nevertheless, it must be conceived as the origin of the road which natural consciousness takes in order to arrive at true and authentic knowing. Differently expressed, phenomenal knowing must be viewed in principle as the starting point from which the individual mind, through various stages and together with other individual minds, ascends to *the* Mind, who knows in full self-experience what He is in Himself. In this sense Hegel's phenomenology itself is not yet science of the Absolute but only the approach leading from phenomenal knowing to an absolute knowing of Absolute Mind.[6]

Husserl and Descartes. When we speak today of phenomenology, we

---

[3] I. Bocheński, *Die Zeitgenössischen Denkmethoden,* München, 1954, p. 22.

[4] J. Hyppolite, *Genèse et structure de la phénoménologie de l'esprit,* vol. I, Paris, 1946, p. 10.

[5] G. Hegel, *Phänomenologie des Geistes,* ed. J. Hoffmeister, Hamburg, 1952, p. 66.

[6] Hegel, *ibid.,* pp. 66 f.

no longer understand this expression in the sense of Hegel, even though it remains true that the phenomenological writings of contemporary authors bear an Hegelian imprint. Anyone who wants to arrive at a clear understanding of the essence and aim of phenomenology cannot avoid studying the background of this movement as painted by Hegel in his *Phenomenology of Mind*.[7] Despite its actuality, the phenomenological movement is also, at least in part, a historical phenomenon.

Nonetheless, when contemporaries speak about phenomenology, the name that arises spontaneously is that of Edmund Husserl. Yet it is not easy to express Husserl's idea of phenomenology. The reason lies in the fact that hitherto only a relatively small part of his writings have been published, and most of these publications are more concerned with picturing an ideal program than with its execution. Moreover, the phenomenological analyses which Husserl has actually made seem to eliminate that ideal program and its implied self-interpretation, although Husserl himself does not seem to have realized this.

According to the grandiose program which Husserl drew up for his philosophical life and which he described extensively in his *Ideas* and his *Cartesian Meditations,* he viewed his own work as a radicalization of Descartes' demand that all philosophical knowledge be founded in an absolutely certain insight, raised above every possibility of doubt. But in many points his numerous and extensive analyses appear to contradict his endeavor to think radically about the modern problematics of the subject.[8] In these analyses this problem reveals itself as a pseudo-problem, so that Husserl's standpoint in this matter comes very close to that of Heidegger and Merleau-Ponty.[9]

Philosophy as a Rigorous Science. Later we will revert to this point. For the present we wish to emphasize that by means of his phenomenology Husserl wanted to arrive at "philosophy as a rigorous science."[10] Explaining this standpoint, Husserl stressed that, since its beginning in Greece, philosophy has always aspired to be an all-encompassing, intellectually justified knowledge of all that is.[11] For this reason

---

[7] A. de Waelhens, "Phénoménologie husserlienne et phénoménologie hégélienne," *Revue philosophique de Louvain,* vol. 52 (1954), pp. 234-249.

[8] L. Landgrebe, *Philosophie der Gegenwart,* Bonn, 1952, pp. 31-40.

[9] Merleau-Ponty, *Phenomenology of Perception,* pp. 60, 243, 365, 376.

[10] E. Husserl, "Philosophie als strenge Wissenschaft," *Logos,* vol. 1 (1910-11), pp. 289-341.

[11] Husserl, *Ideen zu einer reinen Phänomenologie und phänomenologischen Philosophie,* 3 vols., Den Haag, 1950-52; *Nachwort,* vol. 3, pp. 138-139; *Die Krisis der europäischen Wissenschaften und die transzendentale Phänomenologie. Eine Einleitung in die Phänomenologie,* Den Haag, 1954, p. 66.

philosophy is not a matter of feeling or of a more or less fanciful building of systems according to subjective views.   Every cultural period and every system has endeavored to realize this essential aim of philosophy in its own way, but Husserl seriously wanted to attain the goal by means of his phenomenology.[12]   Through a rigorously critical and systematic investigation, Husserl's phenomenological philosophy wanted to attain absolutely valid knowledge of things.[13]

Accordingly, by virtue of its essential aim, philosophy wants to be a "rigorous science."   One should keep in mind, of course, that the scientific character of philosophy differs entirely from that of the sciences of nature and of the mind.[14]   Unlike philosophy, these sciences usually have at their disposal an elaborate apparatus of refined methods.   Thus a superficial spectator can easily get the impression that philosophy is less scientific.   On closer inspection, however, it appears that all non-philosophical sciences start from a complex of presuppositions which are not clarified in these sciences themselves.[15]   Philosophy, on the other hand, does not want to leave anything unsolved; it wants to reduce everything to primary "presuppositions" which do not need to be clarified because they are immediately evident and cannot even be clarified.   It is only in this sense that philosophy as the "science of ultimate grounds" is a rigorous science.[16]

The Natural Attitude.   Thus we see that, according to Husserl, we must make a clear distinction between philosophy and non-philosophical sciences.   The latter flow from the "natural attitude," while the former are born from an entirely different attitude of mind, a philosophical attitude.   In the natural attitude man's perception and thinking are wholly turned toward things, which are given to us as unquestionably obvious and, depending on our standpoint, appear now in this way and now in that.   Among all our acts that refer to things perception is the

---

[12] Husserl, "Entwurf einer 'Vorrede' zu den 'Logischen Untersuchungen,'" *Tijdschrift voor Philosophie,* vol. 1 (1939), pp. 117 and 132; E. Fink, "Die phänomenologische Philosophie Edmund Husserls in der gegenwärtigen Kritik," *Kantstudien,* vol. 38 (1933), p. 340.

[13] Husserl, *Ideen, Nachwort,* vol. 3, pp. 138-141.   For this whole question see also H. Boelaars, "Husserls reducties en haar betekenis voor het thomisme," *Tijdschrift voor Philosophie,* vol. 6 (1944), pp. 334-335.

[14] Fink, "Das Problem der Phänomenologie Edmund Husserls," *Revue internationale de philosophie,* vol. 1 (1938-39), pp. 240-242.

[15] Husserl, *Ideen,* vol. 1, pp. 57-59 and 136-137.

[16] Husserl, "Philosophie als strenge Wissenschaft," *Logos,* vol. 1, p. 340; *Ideen, Nachwort,* vol. 3, pp. 159-162.

most original. What perception offers to us we express in judgments, first in singular judgments, and then in universal judgments. From these judgments we proceed through induction and deduction to new knowledge. "In this way natural knowledge makes progress. Constantly more encompassing, it lays hold of hitherto obviously existing and given reality whose extent and content, elements, relationships and laws are to be more and more investigated."[17] In this way the various sciences of the natural attitude have arisen. Because of the success they have attained in the course of the centuries, those who assume the natural attitude feel no need to ask any question concerning the possibility of knowledge and science or concerning their proper meaning.[18]

Moreover, in the natural attitude one tacitly assumes that we are in a world through which our mind can roam at will and in which we can consider any part we want, without changing the objective nature of what we consider. According to this view, the object-pole of our knowing is an objectively existing, fully explainable world that can be expressed in exact, objective laws. This "objective" world exists wholly in itself and possesses a rationality that can be fully understood. The subject, on the other hand, is pure consciousness; it is fully transparent to itself and faces that rational world, which it can know objectively as it is in itself.

This idea of a single, objective, absolute, autonomous and real world implies also that each of the different sciences has to occupy itself with a part of reality. Otherwise it would not be possible to explain the differences of these sciences because, in this view, there is no reason at all to defend a difference in method. Hence it stands to reason that all sciences together have to constitute a single objective synthesis. An essential difference between philosophy and the other sciences is not even possible.[19]

Husserl protests against such views. "Philosophy," he says, "lies in an entirely different dimension. It needs entirely new starting points and an entirely new method, which is in principle different from those of any 'natural' science."[20] "A philosophy [can] not naively begin at once, like the positive sciences do, which base themselves on the presupposed

---

[17] Husserl, *Die Idee der Phänomenologie,* Den Haag, 1950, p. 18.
[18] Husserl, *ibid.,* pp. 17-19.
[19] Husserl, *Die Krisis* . . . , pp. 18-20.
[20] Husserl, *Die Idee* . . . , p. 24.

foundation of experience of the world as something that is pre-given as obviously existing."[21]   "Its aim as philosophy implies a radicalism of foundation, a reduction to absolute presuppositionlessness, a fundamental method through which the philosopher at the beginning secures an absolute foundation for himself."[22]

The Original Intuition. Husserl seeks the ultimate foundation of all our rational assertions in an immediate vision, i.e., an original intuition of the things themselves concerning which we want to make a statement. His call, "Back to the things themselves," then, means that we must return to the immediate, original data of our consciousness. That which manifests itself there in "bodily presence" is apodictically evident. It does not need any further foundation, but is true and certain.[23]

Accordingly, Husserl does not see the ultimate root, the radical and absolute starting point of philosophy, in any single basic concept, in any single fundamental principle, in one simple *cogito,* but in an entire field of original experiences.[24] His philosophy is a phenomenology precisely because it has as its starting point a field of primordial phenomena. Within this field Husserl does not want any induction or deduction but solely intuition on the basis of a very exact analysis and description.[25] None of the methods used by the other sciences can be of value here, because they have to presuppose something in addition to what is actually given, while in the field of primordial phenomena presuppositions are simply inconceivable. The fundamental principle, then, applying to this field is "that every originarily giving intuition is a legitimate source of knowledge, that everything which presents itself to us originarily in 'intuition,' so to speak in its bodily presence, has to be taken simply as what it presents itself to be, but only within the limits in which it presents itself."[26]

Intuition, however, implies that subject and object are present to each other on the same level. Hence the intuition of the "origins and beginnings" demands that we first try to arrive at the "lowest field of work," in which these foundations are immediately present to our knowing "I." Husserl thinks that his "reductions" can lead us to this

---

[21] Husserl, *Ideen, Nachwort,* vol. 3, p. 160.
[22] Husserl, *ibid.,* p. 160.
[23] Husserl, *Ideen;* vol. 1, pp. 42-44, 50-53; *Die Idee* . . . , pp. 29-32.
[24] Husserl, "Philosophie als strenge Wissenschaft," *Logos,* vol. 1, p. 341; *Die Krisis* . . . , p. 104; *Cartesianische Meditationen und Pariser Vorträge,* Den Haag, p. 69 (see also pp. 57-72).
[25] Husserl, "Philosophie als strenge Wissenschaft," *Logos,* vol. 1, p. 341.
[26] Husserl, *Ideen,* vol. 1, p. 52.

field.[27] By reduction he means in general that methodic procedure by which one places oneself in the "transcendental sphere," the sphere in which we can perceive things as they are in themselves, independently of any prejudice. In other words, it is a change of attitude, by virtue of which we learn to see the things we previously thought to perceive, but in a different way, i.e., in an original and radical way. We penetrate deeper into things and learn to see the more profound "layers" behind what we first thought to see.[28]

Eidetic Reduction. Husserl distinguishes a twofold reduction: the "eidetic reduction" and the complex of reductive phases which he labels the "phenomenological reduction."[29] The eidetic reduction leads us from the realm of facts to that of general essences, and the phenomenological reduction makes us pass from the world of realities to that of their ultimate presuppositions.[30] The eidetic reduction, then, is the methodic procedure through which we raise our knowing from the level of facts to the sphere of "ideas." By essence or idea Husserl means here not the "empirical generalities" which provide us with types encountered in experience, but "pure generalities," which put before our mind pure possibilities whose validity is independent of experience.[31]

In the eidetic reduction one proceeds as follows:[32] as a rule, we start with an arbitrarily perceived or fancied individual sample of this or that kind of things. With the aid of memory, modifications in perception, and especially acts of phantasy, we carefully investigate what changes can be made in the sample without making it cease to be the thing it is. Through the most arbitrary changes, which wholly disregard reality as it is and which therefore are best made in our phantasy, the immutable and necessary complex of characteristics without which the thing cannot be conceived manifest themselves. This "invariant"[33] arises automatically and passively because the objects of the different acts partly overlap, but this "pre-constituted" and still imperfect identical content must still be

---

[27] Husserl, *ibid.*, pp. 118-119, 136-149; Fink, "Die phänomenologische Philosophie . . . ," *Kantstudien,* vol. 38, p. 370.

[28] Boelaars, *art. cit.* in footnote 13, pp. 338-339; Husserl, *Ideen,* vol. 1, p. 5 and *Nachwort,* vol. 3, p. 141.

[29] Husserl, *Ideen,* vol. 1, p. 6.

[30] Husserl, *ibid.*

[31] Husserl, *ibid.*

[32] Husserl, "Philosophie als strenge Wissenschaft," *Logos,* vol. 1, p. 315; *Formale und transzendentale Logik,* Halle a.d.S., 1929, pp. 218-221; *Erfahrung und Urteil,* Hamburg, 1954, pp. 409-426.

[33] Husserl, *Formale und transzendentale Logik,* p. 219.

seized in an "actively intuiting grasp."[34]   Through this grasp, the
absolutely immutable and unique *eidos* which governs all individuals of
this species stands before our mind.

Phenomenological Reductions.   In addition to these eidetic reductions, Husserl admits also a complex of phenomenological reductions.
They are sometimes divided as follows:

1. The phenomenological reduction in the strict sense, which is also
called the "bracketing of being."

2. The reduction of the cultural world to the world of our immediate
experience (*Lebenswelt*).

3. The transcendental reduction which is to lead us from the
phenomenal worldly "I" to transcendental subjectivity.[35]

In the following pages we will speak only about the reduction leading
us from the cultural world to the *Lebenswelt* because, in our opinion, it
would be difficult to interpret the other two in a non-idealistic way.[36]
Unsurprisingly, these two do not occur in the works of Heidegger and
Merleau-Ponty.[37]

To continue, when Husserl wants to explain what the phenomenological reduction is in general and how one can best come to realize its
necessity, he begins with an explanation of the concept "intentionality."
His teacher Franz Brentano, who was not unfamiliar with Aristotelian
philosophy, had introduced this concept into modern psychology.   In
Aristotelian philosophy the term "intention" indicates the orientation of
the mind to its object and, in harmony with this orientation, this object
begins to exist in an intentional way in the mind.   For Brentano this
feature of directedness became *the* characteristic of all psychical
activities.   Although Husserl did not follow Brentano in his psychological views, the fact that all consciousness is intentional, that all
consciousness is consciousness-of-something, became for him the core of
his new philosophy.[38]

---

[34] Husserl, *Erfahrung und Urteil*, p. 414.

[35] Boelaars, *art. cit.* in footnote 13, pp. 345-362.

[36] Cf. Kockelmans, "Realisme—Idealisme en Husserls phaenomenologie,"
Tijdschrift voor Philosophie, vol. 20, pp. 395-442 (especially 430-441).

[37] L. Landgrebe, *Phänomenologie und Metaphysik,* Hamburg, 1949, pp. 83-100;
W. Biemel, "Husserls Encyclopaedia Britannica Artikel und Heideggers Anmer-
kungen dazu," *Tijdschrift voor Philosophie,* vol. 12 (1950), pp. 246-280;
Merleau-Ponty, *Phenomenology of Perception,* pp. xi-xiv, 60, 243, 365.

[38] Landgrebe, *op. cit.,* pp. 59-69; Boelaars, "De intentionaliteit der kennis bij
Edmund Husserl," *Bijdragen,* vol. 3 (1940), pp. 111-161 and 221-264; A.

Every act of consciousness, in order to be an act, demands a certain object because every conscious act intends something. Every act is "characterized by what the medieval scholastics called the intentional . . . inexistence of an object."[39] If, then, an act of a certain structure is present, then by that very fact a certain object is also present; moreover, the character of this object is co-determined by the character of the act in which the object appears.[40] The character, therefore, of the known object depends on the character of the act by which it is grasped. The large majority, however, of the intentional acts made by an adult civilized human being are not original acts but derived acts. But if it is universally true that the character of the object is co-determined by the character of the act in which it appears, then it follows that "any kind of being has a way of giving itself that is exclusively its own."[41]

Accordingly, if we want to arrive at the sphere in which things appear to us primordially, we have to find a way to lead us from what manifests itself actually in the derived acts to the original objects of our most primordial acts. For the intentional activity of the adult, civilized man is, generally speaking, extremely complex and, correspondingly, that which is constituted by his tending, i.e., meaning, is built up of a manifold of layers of meaning. As a consequence of this, the total meaning can and has to be analyzed in its various components of meaning, each of which is an intentionality. Husserl, now, speaks of "intentional analysis" in reference to the method used when we go back in our questioning from our derivative cognitive acts and their correlates to the original lived experiences (*Erlebnisse*), in which any being whatsoever primordially appears as itself in its immediate givenness.[42]

The dominant tradition of positive science, in which we have been educated, has imposed on us certain prejudices regarding the supposed original object of experience. It claims that this object is the object as it manifests itself through the exact description and determination of the

---

Diemer, *Husserl, Versuch einer systematischen Darstellung seiner Phänomenologie,* Meisenheim a.Gl., 1956, pp. 45-71.

[39] Husserl, *Logische Untersuchungen,* Halle a.d.S., 1913, vol. 2, pp. 366-367; F. Brentano, *Psychologie vom empirischen Standpunkt,* Leipzig, 1924, vol. 1, p. 124.

[40] Husserl, *Logische Untersuchungen,* vol. 2, p. 372; Boelaars, *art. cit.* in footnote 38, pp. 158-161.

[41] Landgrebe, *Phänomenologie und Metaphysik,* p. 85.

[42] Husserl, *Cartesianische Meditationen,* pp. 66-91; *Die Krisis . . . ,* pp. 116-118 and 173-176; Landgrebe, *op. cit.,* pp. 42-49 and 94-97; P. Ricoeur, "Méthodes et tâches d'une phénoménologie de la volonté," *Problèmes actuels de la phénoménologie,* Paris, 1952, pp. 115-123.

sciences. In fact, however, the object of positive science is an abstraction and an artificial structure in reference to the world of our original experience. If, then, we want to discover the truly original structures of the objects in the various domains of being in order to use them as guide lines in the investigation of the corresponding acts of consciousness, we have to abandon the prejudices of the positive sciences and must try to reach reality as it is immediately given in primordial experience. In other words, we have to return to the world as it manifests itself in primordial experience, we must endeavor to find a "natural" world, the world of immediate experience (*Lebenswelt*).[43] It is the task of the phenomenological reduction to lead us back from the cultural world of the sciences to the primordial world of life. This reduction will have to be used in conjunction with the above-mentioned intentional analyses.

Intentionality. As we have indicated, intentionality is the characteristic property of our consciousness, always directing this consciousness to that which it itself is not. This description needs to be rendered more precise. For one could imagine that, according to Husserl, this intentionality would force consciousness to adapt itself passively to whatever it encounters outside itself in the real world. But that is not what Husserl means. When he says that consciousness essentially tends to that which it is not, he wants to say that it belongs to the essence of our consciousness to form a meaning and consequently to constitute its own objects.

Intentionality, then, does not consist in an external object entering somehow into a relationship with consciousness nor in a relationship arising between two psychical contents in our consciousness. Intentionality has nothing to do with relations between "real" objects, but is essentially an act that gives meaning. Thus the object of any act is an inseparable aspect of the meaning phenomenon itself. In Husserl's philosophy the object appears as essentially determined by the structure of thinking itself; this thinking itself first gives meaning to the object and then continues to orient itself to the pole of identity which it itself has already created. When Husserl speaks of transcendence, he does not begin with the reality of the object but always with the meaning of the object. Hence the intentional analyses ultimately always become constitutive analyses, i.e., analyses which do not indicate how meaning is

---

[43] Merleau-Ponty, *La structure du comportement,* Paris, 1949, p. 235; *Phenomenology of Perception,* pp. 407, 430.

found in the primordial experiences, but which want to explain how the meaning of things is primordially constituted in and through consciousness.[44]

This is not all. Hitherto we have limited ourselves to intentionality in function of a theory concerning meaning. Now, however, we must proceed to a more fundamental consideration and endeavor to determine what a consciousness is which itself is essentially intentional. Here there is no longer question of the intentionality of a simple and determined act (*Akt-Intentionalität*) but of the essence itself of consciousness (*fungierende Intentionalität*).[45] The development of this idea, however, probably leads beyond Husserl into the thought of Heidegger.

In any case, if we want to discover what the essence of intentionality, and consequently of our consciousness, really is, we must try to discover our own real presence to ourselves and our presence to things and the world, which is inseparably connected with this self-presence. Certainly, all consciousness is consciousness-of-something, consciousness of the world and of the things of the world. But of even greater importance seems to be the idea that in every concrete, conscious act the unity of the world appears to be already constituted before this unity is explicitly posited as such in a cognitive act of identification. In that case, the cognitive relationship to the world is evidently no longer, in the proper sense of the term, the most primary relationship between man and world, knowledge itself is then a founded relationship and its necessary orientation to the other-than-itself then appears to be a datum no longer characteristic of knowledge alone.[45] In that case, the constitution of an object in knowledge must be considered rather as a tendency pertaining to knowledge only in a typically derivative sense. But then it also becomes evident that consciousness itself cannot be anything other than openness, directedness to the other, and denial of self-foundation. In this way consciousness appears to be not pure interiority, but should be

---

[44] Husserl, *Ideen*, vol. 1, pp. 134-136, 212-215, 363-380; *Cartesianische Meditationen*, pp. 17-34; *Die Krisis* . . . , pp. 114-116, 146-151, 170-173, 182-193, 207-214; G. Berger, *Le cogito dans la philosophie de Husserl*, Paris, 1941, pp. 92-117, 129-131; A. de Waelhens, "L'idée phénoménologique de l'intentionnalité," in D. M. de Petter, "Het tweede internationaal colloquium over de phenomenologie," *Tijdschrift voor Philosophie*, vol. 18, pp. 727-731; G. Brand, *Welt, Ich und Zeit*, pp. 34-41; Diemer, *op. cit.* in footnote 38, pp. 55-71 and *passim*.

[45] Brand, *op. cit.*, pp. 22-25.

understood as a going-out-of-itself, as ex-sistence. And explicit acts of cognition are only a mode of our human existence based on our being-in-the-world.[46]

2. Intentional and Constitutive Analyses

In the following two chapters we will speak more extensively about Heidegger's conception of existence and knowledge; hence there is no need to dwell here on the above-discussed point. However, for a good understanding of phenomenology as the *method* to be used in Part Two, it seems necessary to dwell somewhat longer on what, above, we have called "intentional" and "constitutive analyses." With Paul Ricoeur we think that most existential phenomenologists, theoretically at least, underestimate the importance of these analyses within a phenomenological philosophy. "If in every problem," he says, "we go straight to the 'existential project' and the 'movement of existence' which carries along all authentically human behavior, we run the risk of disregarding the specific character of the problems, of drowning the contours of the various functions in a kind of indistinct existential monism, which ultimately would induce us to repeat the same exegesis of 'existence' with respect to the imagination, the emotions, laughter, gestures, sexuality, speech, etc."[47]

Summary. To explain more accurately the importance of these analyses, let us first summarize as concisely and as clearly as possible the various points discussed above. The aim of phenomenology as a method is to provide philosophy with an absolute and radical starting point. Following Descartes, Husserl sees this starting point in an *ego cogito,* but for him every *cogito* is essentially the *cogito* of a *cogitatum.* Against Descartes, therefore, Husserl maintains that not only the fact of the *cogito* is an absolute and indubitable datum but that the *cogitatum* also is such a datum, provided this *cogitatum* is taken as it immediately appears in the *cogito.* The absolute and radical starting point of philosophy, therefore, lies not in a single certain thesis (Descartes' *ego cogito*) but in an indefinite number of "theses," provided these theses are taken precisely as they manifest themselves immediately and intuitively in an indubitably certain cogitation.[48]

---

[46] de Waelhens, *loc. cit.* in footnote 44.
[47] P. Ricoeur, *op. cit.* in footnote 42, pp. 115-116.
[48] Husserl, *Die Idee . . . ,* pp. 29-32; *Cartesianischen Meditationen,* p. 11.

The last-named requirement demands that the phenomenologist try to attain the proper sphere before he begins to analyze and describe the content of his *cogito cogitatum*. The method of reduction is to lead him to this sphere. It makes him pass from the realm of derivative acts, marked by our culture and especially by the influence of the sciences, to that of acts which make things present to us "bodily" in an original fashion, in an experience that is characteristic for each type of being. Once he has arrived in the proper sphere, he can begin to analyze and describe accurately whatever manifests itself primordially there to him. This analysis and description have to be noetico-noematic, i.e., in this description and analysis attention must be paid to both the noetic and the noematic aspects of the whole "given," in other words, to both the act in which the *cogitatum* is given and to this *cogitatum* itself which originally appears in this act.[49]

For, if one admits that all consciousness is consciousness-of-something, it is evident that nothing can be said about consciousness unless attention is paid to that of which one became conscious in the various acts. On the other hand, it is obvious that in this way the question about the essence of any be-ing is reduced to that of the modes of consciousness in which the be-ing had to manifest itself *originally* as "this" or "that." The essence of things, therefore, can be determined only by returning in an intentional analysis to the acts of our consciousness in which any be-ing constitutes itself *originally* as "this" or "that." This assertion appears a necessary consequence flowing from the application of the idea of intentionality to human knowledge.

Because all this is of the greatest importance for a correct understanding of intentional analysis, we will dwell a little longer on it. But for the sake of clarity, we will no longer speak about acts of consciousness in an abstract way, but will pay attention to the most important of these acts, the act of perception.[50]

Profiles. When one analyzes a particular act of perception carefully, it becomes at once evident that each act of perception seizes the perceived object only in a certain respect. Expressed in a correlated way, any perceptible thing is always perceived from a determined standpoint, a well-defined viewpoint. Standing in front of the house, I effectively perceive only the facade. The sides and the rear are hidden to me. I

---

[49] Husserl, *Ideen,* vol. 1, pp. 218-221.

[50] In this matter we follow the broad lines suggested by A. Gurwitsch, *The Field of Consciousness,* Pittsburgh, 1964, pp. 202-305.

can, of course, change my standpoint and place myself in a different position with respect to the house. If I do so, I still perceive the same house, but now only in a different respect. No matter how I place myself, I always perceive this house in a determined respect. The perceived gives itself in and through the act of perception only by means of profiles (*Abschattungen*) which are correlated to a determined attitude and standpoint of the perceiver.[51]

Moreover, this determined standpoint, with respect to the house, refers intrinsically to other possible standpoints, just as the effectively perceived aspects refer intrinsically to other possible perceptible aspects. While I perceive the facade of the house, I am aware that I could also perceive the other sides by simply changing my standpoint. For each perceptible object it is true that its perception can take place only in a quasi-infinite series of profiles, corresponding to a quasi-infinite number of possible standpoints.[52]

Noesis—Noema. Let us assume now that I perceive this particular house from the street in front of it so that I can effectively see only its facade. If, subsequently, I want to learn more about this house's exterior appearance, then the only possibility is to have recourse to ever-new "partial perceptions," each of which will manifest separately a certain aspect of this house. What is typical here is the fact that in any such case we will always experience the manifold of profiles as profiles of this particular house. And in a correlate way we experience the manifold of partial perceptions as perceptions of a single thing.

Thus, the perceived thing clearly does not exhaust itself in anyone of its individual profiles, but that which is intended in each of the concrete acts, without, however, being effectively and as such perceived in any particular act whatsoever remains the same in all cases. In this particular act of perception or *noesis* this house effectively manifests itself always in this particular profile when this particular standpoint is assumed; but, nonetheless, each concrete act intends more than this particular profile and aims at the house as a whole. This intended total meaning which is clearly constituted as the perceptional meaning in every particular act of perception of this house, precisely insofar as it manifests itself in this act,

---

[51] Husserl, *Ideen,* vol. 1, pp. 91-95; *Erfahrung und Urteil,* pp. 26-27. For the "theory of profiles" see especially C. Graumann, *Grundlagen einer Phänomenologie und Psychologie der Perspektivität,* Berlin, 1960.

[52] Husserl, *Ideen,* vol. 1, pp. 100-104; W. Luijpen, *Existential Phenomenology,* Pittsburgh, 6th impr., 1966, pp. 97 f.

is called *noema*. This noema explains why every individual act of perception refers to other, possible perceptions of this same house. These perceptions are destined to complement and strengthen the first perception; and, by virtue of them, this first perception is able to appear as a phase of a possible total process.[53] Let us clarify this point somewhat more extensively.

The Process of Perception as Fulfillment (Erfüllung). When different acts of perception are concerned with the same house, we experience all these acts as referring to one and the same thing and, therefore, these distinct acts are in harmony and agreement, although that which is effectively perceived as such differs in all these cases. Despite the fact, however, that the profiles of the separate acts are different, it is clear that these acts cannot be in agreement if the profiles in question do not harmonize in one way or another. Consequently, the fusion of the different individual acts of perception concerning one and the same thing into a total process of perception presupposes, of necessity, that the corresponding profiles fit into a "connected whole." Because the corresponding profiles organize themselves into a single, connected whole, the acts of perception can appear as phases of a total process.[54]

Thus, the unification of the individual acts does not depend on the temporal relationships existing between them. It does not even appear necessary that the acts succeed one another without interruption. In other words, the unification in question does not refer to the acts themselves as psychical events occurring in a phenomenal time, but only to their intentional correlates, i.e., the noemata corresponding to them. Consequently, because the different partial perceptive representations of one and the same material thing constitute a single noematic system, we can explain that the one-sidedness of each individual act is at the same time both experienced and overcome.

The one-sidedness of each particular act of perception of one and the same thing is overcome in the total process of perception only if the different profiles contained in the noematic system successively actualize themselves in and through the corresponding acts in such a way that the thing appears in a manifold of different but harmonious explicit aspects. For in this way each particular perceptive act in which the thing

---

[53] Husserl, *Ideen,* vol. 1, pp. 91-98, 241-249; *Cartesianische Meditationen,* pp. 77-79; Gurwitsch, *op. cit.,* pp. 202-204.

[54] Husserl, *Ideen,* vol. 1, pp. 363-368; *Cartesianische Meditationen,* pp. 87-89; Gurwitsch, *op. cit.,* pp. 204-210.

manifests itself only in a particular aspect implies references to other partial acts in which the thing manifests itself in constantly different but harmonious aspects. Viewed *noematically,* these references are essential features of the perceptive noema in question; and *noetically* considered, they appear as anticipations of new acts destined to complement this particular actual perception. Thus, it is not the temporal succession of the acts that overcomes the one-sidedness of each particular act, but the fact that they confirm, complement and perfect one another. Accordingly, the process of perception, noetically viewed, is a process of fulfillment (*Erfüllung*).[55]

Internal Horizon. Above we have said that in the perceptive noema, i.e., in the thing as it manifests itself to us in and through a given act of perception, by way of a particular profile, a distinction has to be made between that which effectively manifests itself now and is given as such and, on the other hand, the "rest." When we perceive a house, we effectively see only one side of it. Nevertheless, our actual perception has a greater content than what is effectively seen, for aspects that are not effectively perceived always play a role in the noema. Without such factors we would merely see a not-too-sharply-defined surface having a certain color but not the facade of a house. In other words, that which is effectively perceived always appears in the light of data that are not effectively perceived. The complex, now, of the effectively and non-effectively perceived aspects constitutes the perceptive meaning in question.

To express the matter differently, every perceptive noema contains a rigidly defined core which is immediately given in experience and which, moreover, refers to not-immediately given aspects. The whole of the not-immediately given factors, Husserl calls the "internal horizon" of the perceptive noema.[56] We may add that the noematic core refers to the structures of the internal horizon, to a greater or a lesser extent, in proportion to the familiarity we already have with the perceived object. For this reason the internal horizon can be unfolded on the basis of what is here and now effectively perceived, provided this explicitation adheres rigidly to the limits set by that which is effectively perceived.[57]

External Horizon. Finally, we should keep in mind that whatever appears to man in his various acts of perception always manifests itself

[55] Husserl, *Ideen,* vol. 1, 333–353; Gurwitsch, *op. cit.,* pp. 210-213.

[56] Husserl, *ibid.,* pp. 100-101; *Erfahrung und Urteil,* pp. 26-37; Gurwitsch, *op. cit.,* pp. 228-238.

[57] Gurwitsch, *op. cit.,* pp. 238-245.

within a certain context. Every perceived thing or noema, Husserl says, has not only an internal horizon but also its external horizon,[58] for every perceptible object appears to us as a certain figure against a certain background. The house, which I experience as a unit through a quasi-infinite series of profiles, appears really as a house only against the horizon of the street, the park, the square, or the garden in which it stands. A house that is not found in the certain surroundings of which it is a part could never be a real house and could never be perceived as a house. When I direct my attention to this particular house in this street, then this house detaches itself from the background of meanings, but this horizon remains constitutive of the perceived real thing. If I direct my gaze to another house or to the car in front of it, the first house enters again into the horizon and cedes its privileged position to the other object of perception.

Thema and Thematic Field. The same idea can be expressed in a different way. The house is the thema of my perceptive act, and as such it is surrounded by a thematic field consisting of other themata. Something similar applies to other cognitive acts. If, for instance, in logic one makes a certain proposition the object of his study, the thema of a certain complex of explicit acts, then this thema also is surrounded by a thematic field consisting of other propositions and theses which flow from the first or from which the first has been deduced. In general, one can say that the thema of a particular act is that on which the subject at a given moment centers his attention. The corresponding thematic field is the complex surrounding the thema in this act, the total context in which this thema manifests itself in this particular act.

It is to be noted that the thematic field is not simply identical with the field of perception. For the field of consciousness, the field of perception, the external horizon encompasses the totality of everything which in any way whatsoever is co-present in consciousness to a given thema. Therefore, it would be better to make a distinction in the external horizon between those data that are immediately related to the perceived thing (the noema or thema), which together constitute the thematic field; and, on the other hand, those elements which have nothing to do with the thema here and now considered and which therefore could be called the "margin."

The thematic field is very important for a correct view of the thema, for the thema refers to the thematic field, and the field gives to the thema

---

[58] Husserl, *Ideen,* vol. 1, p. 58; *Erfahrung und Urteil,* p. 28.

a certain color and shading or at least co-determines its complete concrete meaning.[59] Thus, the structure of figure—horizon, which A. Rubin discovered in his study about the perception of sketches and figures,[60] and which Merleau-Ponty extended to the entire domain of perception,[61] may be conceived as a general structure of consciousness. The figure—horizon structure is nothing but a special case of the general structure of thema—thematic field.

Function and Importance of the Intentional Analysis. After these brief explanations it should no longer be too difficult to understand the importance of the intentional analyses. The original function and importance of this method lies in its unveiling the implicit aspects contained in the actual states of our consciousness. Generally speaking, it is the method of bringing forward and explicitating meanings, the method of disengaging constituent elements which are implicitly contained in certain actually given meanings.[62] Its application to perception is based on an accurate analysis of that which is here and now given immediately but only implicitly in concrete perception.

If, then, we want to disclose the "meaning of a perception," we must try to explicitate the internal horizon together with the thematic field. This process has both a noetic and a noematic aspect. Noetically considered, this method demands that the thematic field be described as a deciphering of the anticipations of possible new and still potential perceptions. This particular perception, therefore, must be considered in relation to the whole "system" of acts which in one way or another are connected with this concrete perception and which could actuate its virtual content. Noematically considered, the intentional analysis endeavors to make explicit in consciousness all meanings which were only implicitly indicated in the effectively given datum. In fulfilling this function, it takes into account all the essential influences exercised by the internal horizon and the thematic field.[63]

In the preceding pages we have spoken about the act of perception. But any other act in which the subject tends to something can also be

---

[59] Gurwitsch, *op. cit.*, pp. 318-335.

[60] A. Rubin, *Visuell wahrgenommene Figuren*, København, 1921.

[61] Merleau-Ponty, *Phenomenology of Perception*, pp. 3 f., 33-36, 67-72, 280-298, 312-317.

[62] Husserl, *Cartesianische Meditationen*, pp. 83-86. See also the references made in footnote 42.

[63] Gurwitsch, *op. cit.*, pp. 292-295.

subjected to such an analysis, for instance, all cognitive acts based on perception, all affective acts, and strivings. In all these cases the aim is to show, through analysis and description, what this act really is in itself and which object is primordially constituted in this act. Because philosophy is not interested in the concrete as such, the emphasis in these analyses will always fall on the essential structures. The guiding principle for such an analysis is most properly borrowed from the noematic aspect of the total datum. For this reason these analyses are sometimes called "noematic reflections." By carefully "peeling off" the intentionalities which cover and cross one another in the noema, viewed in its connection with the intentional acts aiming at it, we must try to arrive at a radical insight into the total datum.

A philosopher who wants to perform an intentional analysis and is solely or at least primarily interested in the epistemological problems of the positive sciences has, of course, to rely on the derived acts which actually constitute the science in question. Although it would be possible to apply such an analysis immediately to these derived acts, it will, generally speaking, be better if he limits himself to the experiences that are primordial to the science in question. A concrete example may serve to clarify this point. When we ask ourselves what physical science really is and what is meant by nature, as it is considered by physical science, we are faced with the fact that physical science presents itself as a deductive theory or as a complex of deductive theories. Through the syntactic and semantic analyses of contemporary logic it is possible to isolate those acts which occupy a fundamental place in the deductive system. This procedure has the added advantage that the generally complex mathematical formalism in which the scientific theses concerning nature are formulated need not be made part of the intentional analysis. Later we will have an opportunity to revert to this point.[64]

---

[64] Ricoeur, *art. cit.* in footnote 42, pp. 114-117; Husserl, *Ideen,* vol. 2, pp. 1-11. See also our work *Tijd en ruimte,* Haarlem, 1958, pp. 66-69 and the literature quoted there.

CHAPTER THREE

INTENTIONALITY AND EXISTENCE

It is the task of philosophy to disclose the ultimate foundations of being and of our knowledge of being. From its very beginning, moreover, philosophy has always wanted to be perfectly radical in the execution of this task. It wants to be a science characterized by a radical "absence of presuppositions."[65] This aim does not mean, of course, that philosophy wants to begin with nothing or intends to speak only about being and truth. Otherwise, how could it maintain its aim to investigate the ultimate meaning of human existence? How could it ask, What is man? Whence comes man and whither does he go? What is the meaning of his existence? What is his place and his importance in the world? How is he related to non-human things and especially to other human be-ings? If he himself is not the ground of everything that is, how is he related to all be-ings, to being, and to the ground of everything that is?

All these questions have been central questions of philosophy for many centuries. True, philosophy has also directed its questions to other domains, to things of the world, to space, time, science, morality, art and religion. Also it has often formulated its questions in a different way or modified its attitude. Nevertheless, the question of what man is has always remained somehow the cardinal question. Not without justification, therefore, did Max Scheler, reverting perhaps unwittingly to a statement of Kant, say: "In a certain sense all central issues of philosophy can be reduced to the questions of what man is and what metaphysical position man occupies within the whole of being, the world and God."[66]

---

[65] Dondeyne, *Contemporary European Thought and Christian Faith*, Pittsburgh, 2nd impr., 1963, p. 47.

[66] M. Scheler, "Zur Idee des Menschen," *Abhandlungen und Aufsätze*, Berlin, 1925, vol. 1, p. 319; I. Kant, *Werke*, ed. by E. Cassirer, vol. 8, pp. 343-344. Concerning Kant see Heidegger, *Kant and the Problem of Metaphysics*, Bloomington, 1962, p. 217 and M. Buber, *Das Problem des Menschen*, Heidelberg, 1948.

Thus, on the one hand, philosophy aims primarily at being; but, on the other, the question of what man is seems fundamental. How are these two points to be reconciled? According to an important trend of contemporary philosophy, the bond is not difficult to find, for the question of what being is, is most intimately connected with the question of how being can be attained. If being is taken not abstractly but concretely, it seems evident that it can be reached only from the standpoint of the experience that we ourselves are.[67] It appears worth while to dwell somewhat longer on this point. Nevertheless, in doing so, we will limit ourselves to issues that are relevant to our purpose.

1. The Question of Being—Dasein

What is Being? As we have mentioned, since the origin of philosophy the Western world has nearly unanimously considered the question, What is being? as the central issue of philosophy. Everyone thinks that he knows what being is, and for centuries traditional philosophy has occupied itself with this fundamental question. Nevertheless, the question has to be asked again, for traditional philosophy has accepted the provisional understanding gained by Plato and Aristotle as obvious, without making the point again and again "a thematic question of an authentic investigation" and reflecting upon it as such.[68] As a result, many have forgotten the proper problem of philosophy. An authentic philosopher will have to take up the problem where the Greek philosophers left it; otherwise, deceived by the "obvious" reply of the Greeks, he will not even see what the core of the question is and how hollow the traditional concept of being has become.

Although traditional philosophy is right in saying that the concept of being is the most universal concept, nevertheless, this concept implies real problems.[69] It is used in the most divergent senses and, consequently, is not at all evident. Hence it has to be subjected to a systematic investigation. Such an investigation, however, is not possible unless one possesses already some idea about the proper nature of what one seeks. For in the way that any question is asked there is a certain implication regarding the kind of reply that is expected.[70] Thus the fact that the

---

[67] B. Delfgaauw, *Wat is existentialisme?*, Amsterdam, 1950, p. 71; Heidegger *Sein und Zeit*, Tübingen, 1953, p. 2 (English ed., p. 21).

[68] Heidegger, *op. cit.*, pp. 1-2 (English ed., p. 21).

[69] Heidegger, *ibid.*, pp. 2-5 (English ed., pp. 21-24).

[70] Heidegger, *ibid.*, p. 5 (English ed., p. 24).

question is asked about the meaning of being shows that man has some idea what the answer will have to be. As a matter of fact, one can easily ascertain that all normal human be-ings are in the possession of such a provisional understanding,[71] no matter how vague and confused it be. One of philosophy's most important tasks is precisely to remove this vagueness and to explain the factors that have led to it.[72]

The greatest difficulty encountered in this task lies in the fact that demonstrations are largely useless because being is not something "that can be demonstrated."[73] For being cannot be considered from a standpoint lying outside being itself; moreover, every question regarding being necessarily presupposes that one absolutely exclude any radical distinction between the object investigated and the be-ing which investigates. For this reason an adequate study of the problem of being demands a method of its own. As we have seen above, this method is supplied by phenomenology.[74]

Being and Dasein. Accordingly, the ultimate point of interest to the philosopher is being. Being is that which makes be-ings be-ings. Being, therefore, itself is not a be-ing and cannot be reduced to one or the other be-ing. Since being, then, means "the being of be-ings," he who wants to find an answer to the question of being may and has to start with be-ing. Be-ing has to be questioned about its own being. If this be-ing is to disclose the proper characteristics of its own being in a true light, it has first to become accessible as it is in and for itself. As Heidegger expresses it, "The question of being requires, in reference to what is to be interrogated, that the correct approach to be-ings shall have been obtained and secured in advance."[75]

However, there are many be-ings. All of them are called be-ings, but always in a different sense. Whence, then, is the philosopher to start in order to discover the true and proper meaning of being? May one start from just any be-ing, or is there a be-ing having a certain preference with respect to the question we are interested in? If so, what is this be-ing, and in what sense has it priority over the other be-ings?[76] At first sight,

---

[71] Heidegger, *ibid.,* pp. 5, 8, 200 (English ed., pp. 25, 27, 244).

[72] Heidegger, *ibid.,* p. 6 (English ed., p. 25).

[73] Heidegger, same reference. See also G. Marcel, *Journal métaphysique,* Paris, 1935, p. 36; J. Wahl, *Etudes kierkegaardiennes,* Paris, 1949, p. 115.

[74] Heidegger, *ibid.,* pp. 6 and 27 (English ed., pp. 25 and 49).

[75] Heidegger, *ibid.,* p. 6 (English ed., p. 26). As Luijpen correctly remarks (*Existential Phenomenology,* pp. 59 ff.), the being of be-ings is an *original,* but not the *ultimate,* characterization of being.

[76] Heidegger, *ibid.,* p. 7 (English ed., pp. 26 f.).

these questions appear unanswerable. On closer inspection, however, there appears to be one be-ing, and only one, capable of supplying us with such a starting point regarding the question of the meaning of being. That be-ing is the be-ing which can question *itself*—man. Thus, it is only through a profound analysis of human existence or *Dasein* that we can arrive at an understanding of the being of be-ings.[77] In this sense an analysis of human existence is a necessary condition of authentic philosophy: "The analytic of *Dasein* . . . must prepare the fundamental ontological problematic, the question regarding the meaning of being in general."[78]

2. Existence as the Central Reference Point of Existential Phenomenology

Not all phenomenologists will fully accept the above-described position of Heidegger. Yet they agree almost unanimously with him that a careful analysis of *Dasein* constitutes a necessary starting point of philosophy. Any philosophy worthy of the name is somehow rooted in concrete human existence and also is ultimately developed for the sake of understanding and guiding this existence. Despite the fact that philosophy properly aims at being and truth, it may be defined also as that science which searches for a radically founded reply to the question, What is man?[79]

Man Alone "Exists." It is in this sense that Albert Dondeyne[80] describes the contemporary philosophical trend founded by Husserl and Heidegger, which for the sake of convenience is often indicated as "existentialism," as the philosophical current which is dominated by the idea of existence. A brief explanation of what is meant by these terms "existence" and "dominated" may serve to clarify this description. The term "existence" can have a variety of meanings for the existentialists, but as the primitive fact of existential phenomenology it has an accurately defined meaning. It serves not to express that something actually belongs to the realm of existing realities, but to indicate that mode of being which is proper to man and precisely constitutes him a human be-ing. In other words, only man exists.

---

[77] Same references.

[78] Heidegger, *ibid.*, p. 183 (English ed., p. 227).

[79] Dondeyne, *Contemporary European Thought and Christian Faith*, p. 47.

[80] Dondeyne, "Beschouwingen bij het atheistisch existentialisme," *Tijdschrift voor Philosophie,* vol. 13 (1951), pp. 10-21.

Of course, this expression does not mean that apart from man no other beings are, but only that man possesses a mode of being which distinguishes him from all other be-ings. What, then, is special about man's mode of being? It appears to consist in the fact that man, in order to realize himself, has to place himself, as it were, outside himself, he has to "ex-sist." In an original and essential way man is oriented to a world and for this reason every manifestation of his being-man is a mode of being actively related to the world. Human subjectivity is originally and in its innermost essence an intentional and self-"transcendent" being. Only through his familiarity with the world does man realize himself. His being is a being-in-the-world.[81] Man is neither inert matter nor pure interiority. He "ex-sists" and as such he is openness to the world or, more generally, openness of the subject to what the subject himself is not.

Heidegger finds these same ideas in the prefix *Da* of *Dasein* and for this reason he reserves the term *Dasein* for man.[82] This same prefix, moreover, implies the idea of presence (*Anwesenheit*). Human subjectivity is not a locked-in *I*, but manifests itself originally as a "being-with," a "being-open-to." In the same vein, Merleau-Ponty expresses the primitive fact of "existentialism" by the term "presence" (*présence*), because this term makes it very clear that man and the world cannot possibly be conceived separately. It would indeed be impossible to speak of presence unless there be something to which a subject is present, and reversely, a field of presence is meaningless without a subject.[83] For the same reason other phenomenological thinkers use the expressions "encounter" or "dialogue."[84]

All these expressions are meant to indicate that man is not a closed monad, but is originally a being-in-and-to-the-world, and in this dialogue with the world he makes the meaning of things appear in an original way. Only through this familiarity with the world does man become familiar with himself. Man's being, therefore, is a knowing-itself-to-be-present-in-the-world which is present to itself only through this being-in-and-to-the-world. All this Heidegger summarizes in his well-known

---

[81] Heidegger, *ibid.*, p. 53 (English ed., p. 78).

[82] Heidegger, *ibid.*, pp. 11-15, 41-45 (English ed., pp. 31-36, 67-71). Cf. Biemel, "Heideggers Begriff des Daseins," *Studia catholica*, vol. 24, pp. 113-129.

[83] Merleau-Ponty, *Phenomenology of Perception*, p. 430.

[84] Luijpen, *op. cit.*, pp. 36 f.

statement: "The 'essence' of *Dasein* lies in its existence."[85] Thus, the idea of existence appears to be only another term for what Husserl calls the intentionality of consciousness when in his later writings he defines "functioning intentionality" itself as "world-experiencing life" (*Welter-fahrendes Leben*).[86]

The Primitive Fact of Philosophy. For existential phenomenology existence conceived in this way is the primitive fact that dominates all its thinking. In this philosophy existence is the original intuition, the original datum that gives and founds meaning. It is the original meaning-giving experience that is present in all other data of experience and makes it possible for us to discover the meaning of everything that is. For every philosophy is borne by an aspect of intelligibility, by an original light which as a "natural light" is so central, so fundamental, and so all-encompassing that it can throw light on everything that can manifest itself to human consciousness as something endowed with meaning. For existential phenomenology existence, in the above-described sense, is this primordial phenomenon.

We may even say that existence is the primitive fact of philosophy in a twofold sense. First, the mode of being called "existence" cannot be reduced to something else that would be more fundamental, but is the most original datum having meaning. Secondly, this mode of being is primary in the sense that it is the foundation of everything which can ever have meaning and value for man. In other words, existence is also the most original datum that gives and founds meaning. This statement does not mean that man is the creator of everything that is, but implies that all manifestations of human existence and all meanings which the world has for man are to be understood and founded in the light of this idea of existence.[87] Existence, therefore, has here the value of a primary phenomenon that is irreducible to anything else and through which everything else has to be understood.

The philosopher must start from the primary experience of existence, or rather of co-existence, i.e., from his not yet thematically understood being as being-in-and-to-the-world-together-with-others. He must endeavor to explicitate first this primary experience if he is to arrive at a justified view of the most fundamental problems of philosophy. Accord-

---

[85] Heidegger, *ibid.*, p. 42 (English ed., p. 67).

[86] Brand, *op. cit.*, pp. 24-25. For this whole matter see Dondeyne's article quoted in footnote 80, pp. 10-14.

[87] Dondeyne, *art. cit.*, pp. 14-19; Luijpen, *op. cit.*, pp. 34-39.

ingly, one who adheres to the statement that the question of man's being is a central question of philosophy, does not automatically admit that this question is the most important question in every respect. He simply wants to recognize the undeniable fact that all of man's thinking concerning anything whatsoever presupposes a reply to the question of what he himself is.

All this shows that "existentialism" faces a twofold task. If existential phenomenology wants to be a radical way of philosophizing, it is not sufficient to state simply that existence has to be considered the primitive fact of philosophy or to characterize man's being with a few schematic expressions. If existential phenomenology wants to escape the reproach of having *a priori* and arbitrarily selected existence as its primitive fact, it will have to show that existence really is a primary phenomenon. It will have to "prove" that the originality and irreducibility of existence as a meaning-giving reality is undeniable and that any effort to deny it, as is made, e.g., by materialism and spiritualism, implicitly presupposes what it denies.

Moreover, existential phenomenology will have to show in what exactly lies the essence of existence as a primary phenomenon. What is it that constitutes my being properly and originally as a *Da-sein,* as a being that "exists"? In the explicitation of this primary phenomenon it is of the greatest importance that the philosopher does not block his own road through any "dogmatic" *a priori* and render himself unable to recognize as real what everyone calls real.[88]

3. *Materialism, Spiritualism, and Existential Phenomenology*

Materialism. The history of man's reflection upon himself is a search for an equilibrium difficult to attain. On this point especially a materialistic view has for centuries opposed a one-sided spiritualistic view.[89] Materialism endeavors to reduce man to a part of the material cosmos, to a thing in the midst of other things. It considers man the result of processes and forces just as things are the results of processes and forces. Man is nothing other than the product of certain psychical, physiological, and social influences,[90] which determine him from without and make him a thing in the midst of other worldly be-ings.

---

[88] Dondeyne, *art. cit.,* p. 19; Luijpen, *op. cit.,* pp. 38 f.

[89] For what follows here see Dondeyne, *art. cit.,* pp. 10-12; Luijpen, *op. cit.,* pp. 15-25.

[90] Merleau-Ponty, *Sens et Non-Sens,* Paris, 1948, p. 142; *Phenomenology of Perception,* Preface, p. viii.

This view, however, disregards the most characteristic feature of man's being, viz., the fact that man is not merely a part of the world, but primarily experiences himself in this world as in a world-for-him; the world appears to him as full of meanings and by this very fact he experiences his being-in-the-world as a meaningful existence.

On the other hand, it is hardly necessary to point out that the materialistic view contains something true. It accounts for a reality which no one may disregard—namely, the fact that man is whatever he is on the basis of his bodily being and, we may even say, on the basis of a certain materiality. Yet it would seem evident that this fact refers only to one aspect of man's being. The mistake of this materialistic vision of man lies in its refusal to admit any other reality in man than the one that is revealed through its own considerations.

Spiritualism. Spiritualism, on the other hand, emphasizes the fact that man experiences himself as a conscious and free living be-ing, as an *ego,* a subject, a person. Quite correctly, its proponents point out that, without man's subjectivity, things and the world would be meaningless. When things and the world are affirmed, they are affirmed in their being-for-subjectivity. Outside this affirmation, they have, viewed originally, no meaning for us because nothing is affirmed there. Spiritualism, however, exaggerates. It makes the relative priority of subjectivity with respect to the world too absolute. Ultimately, this exaggeration reduces the being of worldly things to the being of the subject, by the subject, and for the subject.

Accordingly, while materialism wholly disregards the importance of subjectivity, spiritualism dissolves the density of the things in the world into the volatility of mere contents of consciousness. The ultimate consequence of this procedure is the reduction of all reality to a function of an all-encompassing *ego,* an absolute mind, or a transcendental subjectivity. As Merleau-Ponty points out correctly, "On the one hand, man is a part of the world, but on the other, he is a consciousness constitutive of the world. Neither view is satisfactory."[91]

Existential Phenomenology. Existential phenomenology wants to overcome the difficulties of both materialism and spiritualism by conceiving man as essentially openness to the world, as existence. "The merit of the new philosophy is precisely that it seeks in the notion of existence the means to conceive the human condition" correctly.[92] As we

---

[91] Merleau-Ponty, works quoted in preceding footnote, pp. 142 and xv f.
[92] Merleau-Ponty, *Sens et Non-Sens,* p. 143.

have indicated above, it is not possible to describe in a sharply formulated definition what exactly is meant here by the term "existence." The term is the philosophical expression of man's primary self-experience in his relationship to the world, and the proper features of this experience cannot be adequately expressed. As Heidegger says, "The definition of this being [*Existenz*] cannot be made by indicating a quidditative 'what.' "[93] We can only speak about the way in which this existence appears. The first and most general characteristic through which man distinguishes himself from other be-ings is the fact that man is the only be-ing which has a relationship to itself. "The self of man," says Kierkegaard, "is a relationship that is related to itself."[94] Jaspers takes over the same expression[95] and Heidegger voices the same idea when he writes: "*Dasein* is a be-ing which in its very being is concerned with this being."[96]

Every relationship to itself, however, presupposes essentially, necessarily, and even equi-primordially a relationship to the other, to the world. For this reason existential phenomenology starts with the primordial experience that we can be ourselves only in interaction with the world. Man, no doubt, is a subject, but he is a subject which posits itself of necessity outside itself in the world. My being-to-myself is essentially a being-in-the-world.[97] Briefly put, being-man is being-in-the-world.[98] Without this essential relationship to the world man cannot be conceived. Whatever man is, is able to do and does, he can do and does only in relationship to the world. This aspect of man cannot be demonstrated. All one can do is point to it,[99] by indicating that it is impossible to think of any real mode of being-man which would not be a mode of being-in-the-world.[100] Accordingly, the expression, "Man exists," means that man's being is a being-conscious-in-the-world; his being is a being-open to the world, a dwelling in the world, a being-familiar with the world.[101]

---

[93] Heidegger, *Sein und Zeit*, p. 12 (English ed., p. 32).

[94] S. Kierkegaard, *Sickness unto Death*, New York, n.d., p. 146.

[95] K. Jaspers, *Philosophie*, Berlin, 1956, vol. 1, p. 15.

[96] Heidegger, *ibid.*, pp. 12, 191, 322 (English ed., pp. 32, 236, 368).

[97] Merleau-Ponty, *Phenomenology of Perception*, p. 407; *Sens et Non-Sens*, p. 143.

[98] Heidegger, *ibid.*, pp. 54-55 (English ed., pp. 80-81).

[99] Merleau-Ponty, *Phenomenology of Perception*, p. xviii.

[100] Heidegger, *ibid.*, pp. 56-57 (English ed., pp. 82-84).

[101] Heidegger, *ibid.*, p. 54 (English ed., pp. 79-80) ; Luijpen, *op. cit.*, pp. 18-19.

Analysis of the meaning of our body also leads us to see existence as expressing the essence of our being-man.[102] This analysis discloses two spheres in our bodily being. On the one hand, there is a dimension in which the world and my body appear to me as an objective whole facing me as a subject. In this quasi-objective perspective my body appears to me as something which I know, influence and control, as if it were a thing among the things of the world. Among all these worldly things my body is the thing that is most of all my own.

There is, however, a second and much more important dimension in which my body does not at all appear as a thing among things, but precisely *as mine,* as merged with the subject which I am, and therefore as primarily pertaining to the side of the subject. In this quasi-subjective perspective I experience my body as the "instrument" of all my intentional acts, which not merely appears itself but also and primarily makes the world appear to me. Thus, opposite the object-body of the positive sciences we must place the subject-body, which we experience in our being-in-and-to-the-world as fused with the subjectivity that we ourselves are. With respect to this subject-body, the object-body is only an abstraction. In other words, we cannot continue to adhere to the idea that what physiology teaches us about the body expresses what *my* body means.[103]

Once this is admitted, it is evident that *my* body is the bridge between myself and my world and that *my* body is the place where I make the world my own.[104] My body, then, lies primarily on the side of the subject, but its most important function is precisely to put me into relation with the world. It opens me up to the world and at the same time determines the standpoint from which I am able and have to approach the world.[105] It maintains my vision of the world, animates and nourishes it.[106] When my body disintegrates, my vision of the world disintegrates at the same time.[107] Hence we must conclude with

---

[102] For what follows cf. R. Kwant, "De geslotenheid van Merleau-Ponty's wijsbegeerte," *Tijdschrift voor Philosophie,* vol. 19 (1957), pp. 223-263; *The Phenomenological Philosophy of Merleau-Ponty,* Pittsburgh, 1963, pp. 11-30; Luijpen, *op. cit.,* pp. 21-23; S. Strasser, "Het wezen van de mens," *Annalen v.h. Thijmgenootschap,* vol. 46 (1958), pp. 18-20.

[103] Merleau-Ponty, *Phenomenology of Perception,* pp. 351 and 431.

[104] Merleau-Ponty, *ibid.,* p. 154.

[105] Merleau-Ponty, *ibid.,* p. 165.

[106] Merleau-Ponty, *ibid.,* p. 203.

[107] Merleau-Ponty, *ibid.,* pp. 282 f; *Structure du comportement,* p. 226.

Merleau-Ponty that "the subject . . . forces his ipseity into reality only by actually being a body and entering the world through that body."[108]

Accordingly, one of the merits of existential phenomenology is that it has put man back in his place in the world and that it has managed to describe the world as a human world. In this philosophy man and the world are not isolated but constitute a unity through reciprocal implication.[109] This view cannot be strictly demonstrated, for there is question of a fundamental idea which, as such, can merely be pointed to. This unity of reciprocal implication will be considered more in detail later.

Even when there is question of my relationship to the others, there is no possibility of strict demonstration. All we can do is explicitate and bring to light an original datum. The effort to do so is not easy, as is evidenced by the fact that different phenomenologists present very divergent descriptions of interhuman relationships. This point, however, is not immediately important to our problem; hence there is no need to delve deeply into it. A few broad indications will suffice with respect to the issues raised in this book.[110]

Accordingly, man is really being-in-and-to-the-world and he is in the world through his body. Yet this world is not exclusively my world, for the worldly meanings I encounter in my world constantly refer me to other human beings.[111] If we analyze several concrete situations, it becomes immediately evident that the system of meanings which has part of its origin in my existence is also permeated with actual and possible meanings whose origin I am not. *My* world appears to be not exclusively mine: "The world of *Dasein* is 'with-world' (*Mitwelt*)."[112] Because man and world constitute a unity through reciprocal implication, the fact that the world of others has meaning also for me implies that my existence is a co-existence with others. My encounter with this world manifests itself as our encounter, my world is our world.[113]

---

[108] Merleau-Ponty, *ibid.,* p. 408.

[109] R. Kwant, "Menselijke existentie en geschiedenis volgens het wijsgerig denken van Maurice Merleau-Ponty," *Alg. Ned. Tijdschrift v. Wijsbegeerte en Psychologie,* vol. 46 (1953-54), p. 234.

[110] For what follows see Luijpen, *op. cit.,* pp. 175-195, who speaks also at length about the body as intermediary.

[111] Heidegger, *Sein und Zeit,* p. 117 (English ed., p. 153).

[112] Heidegger, *ibid.,* p. 118 (English ed., p. 155).

[113] Luijpen, *op. cit.,* p. 178.

The same idea imposes itself when we endeavor to explicitate the meaning of the subject-pole of our existence. It is not possible to find any aspect of our being-man in which we are fully alone. The existence of others always plays a role in my existence. If I want to think of myself as I really am, then I have to think also of the others, for they have contributed and still contribute to the reality which I am. I have come from others, have been nourished and educated by others, speak a language which others have formed.[114]

We realize that these few remarks are extremely elementary. However, to prevent our study from becoming too long in a point that is not of immediate relevance to the scope of this book, we do not want to dwell longer on it. Our intention was merely to note that man not merely develops his existence in connection with the world, but his being-in-and-to-the-world is essentially a being-together-with-others.

4. Subjectivity and Existence

Embodied Subjectivity. To be man, we have said, is essentially and fundamentally to exist, i.e., to be oriented to a world, together with others. Several points, however, still need to be clarified. Hitherto, for example, we have often used the terms "subjectivity" and "existence" more or less indiscriminately and, even when the two terms were placed in opposition, not enough attention was paid to their distinction. While it is true that man's typical way of being may be indicated by both terms "subjectivity" and "existence," nonetheless, it is obvious that the two expressions do not mean exactly the same. Yet the central problem of existential phenomenology lies not so much in the distinction between the concepts expressed by these two terms as in the question of how both ideas can be realized at the same time in a single be-ing. How is it possible that subjectivity, despite the most undeniable demands of its own mode of being, nonetheless is somehow committed to exteriority?[115]

In the course of history man has generally been conceived as a subject. Interiority is essential to man. Although this interiority has always been thought of as pure, it appears in fact to be interiority of something; in fact, it exists only as an *intentional* consciousness. The subject which I

---

[114] W. Luijpen, "Phaenomenologie van het recht," *Annalen v.h. Thijmgenootschap,* vol. 46, p. 297.

[115] For what follows see A. de Waelhens, "Subjektiviteit an existentie," *Tijdschrift voor Philosophie,* vol. 6, pp. 283-296.

am *conceives* itself as interiority, but *experiences* itself only as an attempt at interiorization. In this attempt pure interiority seems to recede from us in direct proportion to our efforts to attain it. We want to transcend, so it appears, objects and externality in order to be able to affirm the subject in its active selfhood. In this transcendence we experience at first existence and body, presence and thing, as non-distinct. For, to our spontaneous consciousness, to be real means to be in fact here and now, and to be here and now in fact means to have a body. On closer inspection, however, my entrance into the phenomenal realm does not exhaust my being, but is only a way in which my being strengthens itself. Through its embodiment subjectivity partakes of reality, but nevertheless, this bond does not express the fullness of what subjectivity is.

Several important conclusions follow from the fact that every human subject is of necessity an embodied subject, from the fact, therefore, that all human subjectivity is necessarily a "worldly" subjectivity and in its concreteness arises only through its *Dasein*. First of all, no one can be conscious of his entrance in the world; we always find ourselves as "already there"; we have been "thrown" unfreely into being, and our being is for us always an uncertain gift. Secondly, subjectivity and existence can never merge fully because our interiority is burdened with a fundamental and irreducible "eccentricity." Although man tends to perfect self-possession, as demanded by the idea of the pure subject, he can never attain it since by virtue of his existence man is constantly driven outside. Here lies the tragedy of every human subject: the core of his being, which man irresistibly wants to find in himself because of his subjectivity, can be found only outside himself. As a result man becomes clearly aware of his fundamental finiteness. If one considers within this framework primarily either subjectivity or existence, our body appears to be either the enemy plotting our perdition or the ally without whom our self-affirmation cannot attain full bloom.

Thus, human subjectivity, in its attempted interiorization, is firmly glued to the other-than-I, the world, which it is forced to take up into itself. Our whole mental life implies the admission of the other-than-I because this life can be maintained only by feeding on this other. One can see here the danger to which materialism and one-sided spiritualism have succumbed: in his attempted interiorization man can lose himself by fully surrendering to the other or, on the other hand, he may refuse to recognize the necessity of transcendence.

Radical Intentionality. Accordingly, intentionality, which fascinated Husserl throughout his life, is correctly ascribed by Heidegger, Sartre, and Merleau-Ponty primarily to man's being itself. Our consciousness, Husserl argued, is always and of necessity consciousness of something; and this something, as such, is not consciousness itself. Consciousness is essentially directed to the other, intentional. In addition to this "act intentionality," which it also admits, existential phenomenology, following Husserl's later "functioning intentionality," recognizes a more fundamental form of intentionality. This form of intentionality not merely expresses that man in his acts of knowing is of necessity directed to something else, but primarily wants to indicate that being-man itself implies an essential relationship to the world and that this intentional relationship of being is the proper and ultimate root of all meaning.[116]

Concerning this form of intentionality Merleau-Ponty says that man is nothing else than dwelling in the world, and that there exists no other world for him than the world in which he dwells. We are a presence to the world and the world is our field of presence. Human presence and worldly field of presence together form a single structure. This idea is nothing but a consistent application of intentionality.[117] Accustomed as we are to a natural attitude, such a statement will always cause us difficulties. But if, through a phenomenological reduction, we pass from the natural attitude to a "transcendental" attitude, our gaze meets an original phenomenal field in which alone man and the world manifest themselves in their original appearance.[118] In that attitude the proper meaning of the above-quoted words will become at once clear to us, because in that field man appears as in-and-to-the-world, as project of the world.[119] We will see there that there is nothing in man that escapes from his being-in-the-world. No matter how deep one penetrates into human subjectivity, he will always find there the world, since the world permeates the very heart of subjectivity.[120]

Man is an intention that has entered the world and his entire being is encompassed by dwelling in the world. Man, then, is originally a real

---

[116] Brand, *Welt, Ich und Zeit,* pp. 22-25; Merleau-Ponty, *Phenomenology of Perception,* pp. 418-419, footnote 5 of p. 121, Preface, pp. viii-xxi.

[117] Merleau-Ponty, *ibid.,* p. 430.

[118] Kwant, "De zingedachte van Maurice Merleau-Ponty," *Bijdragen,* vol. 16, pp. 16-17.

[119] Merleau-Ponty, *ibid.,* pp. 406-407.

[120] Merleau-Ponty, *ibid.,* p. 408 and 430.

entrance into a real world. He may discover many characteristics in himself, but all of them are merely modes of being connected with the world. Man is an interplay of question and answer with the world. Our relationship with the world, then, is not merely a cognitive relationship but permeates our entire being. We ourselves are a manifold question to the world and the world is for us the manifold reply to our manifold question. Man is worldly down to the inmost of his essence and, on the other hand, there is for him no other world than this world within the sphere of intentionality.[121] Man and the world are one, but, on the other hand, human subjectivity has characteristics of its own, even though these are nothing other than the ways in which man dwells in the world. Man, for example, is consciousness, but he knows himself only in interaction with the world; man is free, but his freedom is the way in which he involves himself in the world.

As man is permeated with the world, so the world is permeated with man.[122] For how could I conceive a world, divorced from man's presence? By the very fact that we aim at something, intend or think of something, this something exists within our field of presence. A world which would not be a world-for-us is simply unthinkable for us.[123] A phenomenologist, therefore, is not a realist in the sense that he accepts a world existing outside the presence which we ourselves are, but on the other hand, he is not an idealist for he views man himself as nothing other than being-in-the-world. Man and world, more generally, subject and object, are merely two abstract aspects of a single structure, viz., presence.[124]

Intentionality and Meaning. Man and world constitute a unity through mutual implication. In the original presence there are two poles, but these poles necessarily imply each other, they necessarily have a dialectic relationship. Any attempt to disengage one of these poles is an abstraction, but on the other hand, any identification of the two disregards the proper function of these two elements of a single structure.

---

[121] Merleau-Ponty, *ibid.,* pp. 428-430; Heidegger, *Sein und Zeit,* p. 366 (English ed., p. 417).

[122] Merleau-Ponty, *ibid.,* p. 333.

[123] Merleau-Ponty, *ibid.,* p. 320. Cf. also Kockelmans, "Het standpunt van de phaenomenologie met betrekking tot de vraag over de verhouding tussen zijn en verschijnen," *Tijdschrift voor Philosophie,* vol. 22, pp. 544-587.

[124] Merleau-Ponty, *ibid.,* pp. 430 f.

The one is not without the other and cannot be conceived without the other; nevertheless, the two are not identical.[125]

It is in man's living of this fundamental intentionality that meaning originates. Meaning is the result of the encounter between man and the world, an encounter in which both are essentially involved. Meaning is the ultimate noema of our most original noesis, which is our existence itself. This is the reason why phenomenology constantly speaks about meaning in a dual fashion. On the one hand, it claims that all meaning is constituted by consciousness, but on the other, it appears that consciousness is not simply constitutive of meaning since, in its very giving of meaning, it is always and even essentially the recipient of meaning. On the one hand, there is an essential relationship between meaning and existence, but on the other, there is also a unity of reciprocal implication between meaning and "matter," by virtue of which the meaning has always and of necessity a worldly character. Everywhere meaning is connected with existence, but always also are meaning and world interwoven. On the one hand, the meaning of things is permeated with our being-man, but on the other, the meaning is always present in the world also.[126]

Meaning, therefore, is inseparably connected with *our* dwelling in the *world*. It is never given ready-made in a world-without-man and, therefore, it can never impress itself on a passive human consciousness through some kind of unintelligible causal influence. It is not pre-given as an immanent idea which would exteriorize itself in the world. Meaning, then, as direction for our original intentions, neither enters man from the world nor the world from man. Meaning arises only in the encounter of man and the world and exists only in that encounter. It arises and exists only in an interplay of question and answer. We find the question in the world but it is still implicit and vague. Through my reply, which itself is a question, the first question becomes sharper so that a more accurate answer becomes possible. Meaning arises in a dialectic relationship between man and the world, but it is not possible to say which of the two first begins the "interplay" and which of the two first gives meaning to the other. It is likewise impossible to separate the parts

---

[125] Merleau-Ponty, *ibid.*, p. 429. Concerning the preceding matters cf. also Kwant, "Transcendeert Merleau-Ponty het realisme?" *Tijdschrift voor Philosophie,* vol. 16, pp. 244-249, and his article quoted in footnote 109, pp. 233-235.

[126] Kwant, article quoted in footnote 118, pp. 1-2, 11-16, 16-22.

which man and the world have in the constitution of meaning, for their compenetration is original here.[127]

Accordingly, in phenomenology intentionality, as the root and origin of all meaning, does not indicate primarily a cognitive relationship but a relationship of being. "The relationship of the subject and the object," says Merleau-Ponty, "is no longer that cognitive relationship, spoken of by classical idealism, in which the object always appears as constructed by the subject, but a relationship of being through which the subject, paradoxically, is . . . its world."[128] What in common parlance is spoken of as knowledge is for this idea of intentionality merely a special mode of our being-in-the-world. The characteristic feature of this mode of being-in-the-world is that man limits himself here to observing the world, without being totally involved in it. It is a deficient way of being of the subject, which lets us encounter the worldly be-ing only in its pure *eidos*.[129]

Such a contemplative looking-at always implies a certain orientation and attitude with respect to things, for the be-ing that is encountered in this way is always viewed from a certain standpoint. Thus, in his prescientific knowledge and in the science resulting from this knowledge, man receives a new ontological relationship to the world, a relationship that is distinct from the one which manifests itself, prior to any explicit cognitive activity, in man's own being.[130] "Knowing is a mode of *Dasein* which is founded in being-in-the-world."[131] We will dwell more extensively on this point in the next chapter.

5. *Transcendence and Project—Freedom*

In the preceding pages we have occasionally used the expressions "transcendence" and "project." A few words should be devoted here to these elementary ideas.[132]

To be man, we have said, is essentially and fundamentally to exist.

---

[127] Kwant, *ibid.,* pp. 22-23.

[128] Merleau-Ponty, *Sens et Non-Sens,* pp. 143-144.

[129] Heidegger, *Sein und Zeit,* p. 61 (English ed., p. 88).

[130] We presuppose here, therefore, that our being-in-the-world itself contains a certain "knowledge." However, this "practognosis" differs from our predicative knowledge. When people speak of knowledge, they usually refer to the latter type.

[131] Heidegger, *op. cit.,* p. 62 (English ed., p. 90) ; see also pp. 59-62 (English ed., pp. 86-90).

[132] For what follows cf. Luijpen, *op. cit.,* pp. 266-281.

Existence says intentionality and intentionality implies the giving of meaning. As meaning-giving existence, man manifests himself also as freedom.

Negative Aspect of Freedom. The term "freedom" contains both a negative and a positive aspect.[133] Negatively, freedom expresses the absence of necessity. A material thing is not called free because in its being and in all its manifestations it reveals itself as the result of necessary, causally determining processes. No matter what example is chosen to illustrate this point, the fundamental truth always remains that freedom implies the absence of necessity. If, on the other hand, we consider being-man again as being-in-the-world and as intentionality, we see that man must be called freedom because, through his openness to the world and his intentionality, he transcends being-necessitated. True, there are many aspects in man which point to the fact that he is also the necessary result of determining processes. Nevertheless, the total being of man transcends this necessity because existence and intentionality essentially imply self-transcendence.

It should be evident that we are not speaking here about freedom as a property of man's human actions. Freedom, as envisaged here, is concerned with the very being of man on the proper level of his being-human. The being of man itself is to-be-free. It is only on the basis of this fundamental freedom that the freedom of human action can be fully understood.[134]

Positive Aspect of Freedom. Man's freedom, however, implies not merely an absence of necessity, but positively expresses a certain autonomy. Not everything man is, is the result of processes and forces, but the being of man is also a self-being. Man's being is not merely being a part of the cosmos, but he is also subject, subsistence, selfhood, and person. Freedom expresses that mode of being which makes it possible for us to escape the grip of nature, of both nature around us and nature implied by our own being. Freedom means indeed, in the first place, the possibility of saying "No" to nature. But a positive aspect of my freedom is rooted in this negative aspect. In the possibility I have to

---

[133] Dondeyne, "Truth and Freedom," *Truth and Freedom,* by Louis de Raeymaeker and Other Professors of the University of Louvain, Pittsburgh, 2nd impr., 1955, p. 34; A. de Waelhens, "Linéaments d'une interprétation de la liberté," *Liberté. Actes du 4e congrès des sociétés de philosophie de langue française,* Neuchâtel, 1949, p. 82 (quoted by Luijpen, *op. cit.,* p. 266).

[134] Luijpen, *op. cit.,* pp. 266-268.

escape the grip of nature there reveals itself the positive aspect of my fundamental openness, by virtue of which I am able to orient myself to the world, to my future, to draw up plans and bring them to realization, to make a project of myself and the world, thus giving meaning to things and to my own being.[135]   In this context the term "meaning" evokes the idea of direction, and direction gives rise to the concepts of "transcendence" and "project."   It is only through an analysis of these ideas of transcendence and project that the positive side of our freedom can be clarified.

Situated Freedom.   It is important that from the very beginning we clearly realize the non-absolute character of human freedom, for the assertion that man's freedom is absolute would go contrary to all known facts.   While man is an autonomous subject, he is not an isolated subjectivity.   Man's *I* can posit itself only in relationship to the other: to be man is to exist, to be in-the-world, intentionality, to be situated. When above we spoke of man as being-in-the-world and as intentionality, we briefly referred to man's limitation by the world and his being-situated in and through the world.   Something more has to be said about this limitation now.

In his existence man is always placed in a certain constellation of factors.   He knows that this constellation is "already" there and that it expects him to reply to it in a determined fashion.   Hence, to-be-situated is not something superadded which would affect man's being only from time to time, but being-man, as being-in-the-world, is essentially a being-in-a-situation.[136]   Man can never rid himself from his bond to a particular situation.   At any moment of his life he finds himself in a situation.   This situation is not fully under his control, it does not always take into account his desires, needs and plans, but often appears to him as something strange and even hostile.   This situation is determined by man's surrounding world (*Umwelt*), but also and just as essentially by his body, his past, and his facticity, i.e., by the fact that he always discovers himself as "already" being there, even though he has not known, willed and chosen this being.   In other words, his being is for him a fact and at the same time a duty.

This situation, of course, can constantly change.   In his freedom man can actively interfere in his situation, he can take it up and modify it, but he can never fully escape from the grip of his situation.   As Jaspers

---

[135] Luijpen, *op. cit.*, pp. 266-269.
[136] Merleau-Ponty, *Phenomenology of Perception,* p. 408.

expresses it, "Since *Dasein* is a being in situations, I can never get out of one situation without entering into another."[137]   Hence man's freedom and the autonomy of being implied in this freedom are merely relative, for man is not what he is without his body and without the world.   His freedom cannot be divorced from a physical, biological, historical, and social situation.   If we want to speak accurately, we should not conceive this situatedness as a limitation of freedom, for otherwise we would still imply that this freedom "in itself" is an absolute freedom.   The situation, as Merleau-Ponty says, is not a limitation of freedom but the sphere in which alone freedom can become real.[138]

Transcendence.   Reflecting on the implications of man as "engaged" subjectivity and as situated freedom, one sees that man's involvement with the world by way of his body contains two apparently exclusive aspects.   On the one hand, man is necessarily tied to the conditions of his bodily being, but on the other, subjectivity is neither the world nor the body.   On the one hand, man is essentially determined by his facticity, but on the other, through his freedom he is also openness.   Thus, man is always "already" rooted in the constituted, the given, in facticity, but at the same time he also actively takes up this facticity.

Merleau-Ponty uses the term "transcendence" to indicate the compenetration of these two aspects, of being-situated through facticity and its actively being-taken up through subjectivity.   "We call 'transcendence,'" he says, "that movement by which existence takes up and transforms a *de facto* situation."[139]   Contrary to Marcel and Jaspers, therefore, Merleau-Ponty and Heidegger do not conceive transcendence as a necessary relationship to a transcendent object, but as a form that is not yet determined with respect to content, a form in which and through which human existence points beyond itself.   Existence is not a mode of being which reposes in itself and can be understood and defined in itself, but points of necessity beyond itself and therefore transcends itself.[140]

Project.   One who says that man is free implies that man is what he is not and that he is not what he is.[141]   Hence man's freedom expresses not so much that man *is* as that he *has to* be.   Man's being is a task and a

---

[137] Jaspers, *Philosophie*, vol. 2, p. 203.

[138] Kwant, "De mensopvatting van Maurice Merleau-Ponty," *Theologische week over de mens,* Nijmegen, 1958, p. 53.

[139] Merleau-Ponty, *op. cit.*, p. 169.

[140] Luijpen, "Phaenomenologie van de vrijheid," *Tijdschrift voor Philosophie,* vol. 20, 621-634; *Existential Phenomenology*, pp. 265-313.

[141] Sartre, *Being and Nothingness,* New York, 1956, p. 137.

commission in the world. As long as man is authentically and genuinely man, his own being is a task and consequently in principle still unfinished. True, man can disregard the character of commission implied in his being-in-the-world, but in that case he also renounces his authentic being. He then gives himself the mode of being of a thing, which essentially is a mode of lying "crushed upon itself."

Man's being, however, cannot consist of a "having to be" if it does not also imply a "being able to be."[142] That being-man implies such a being-able-to-be should be evident. For, no matter what the concrete situation is in which man finds himself, the man who he actually is always contains a possibility of being different. My actual health, my actual knowledge, my profession, the place I occupy in society, as well as my failures and my illness, all disclose real possibilities to me. This being-able to be is so closely connected with man that without this aspect there can be no question of being-man. On the other hand, this being-able-to-be is always a possibility within a given situation. Man's ability to be always implies, of necessity, a limiting facticity. Man is the oppositional unity of facticity and ability to be.

To express this unity-in-opposition, modern philosophers use the term "project."[143] "The project," says Heidegger, "is the existential state-of-being of the leeway which the factical being-able-to-be has."[144] Man is a project. Unlike a thing, he is not fettered to his facticity, but his freedom allows a certain amount of leeway to his ability to be within the reality of his limiting facticity. Because of this leeway, man is always "ahead of himself." "Ontologically, being toward one's ownmost being-able-to-be means that in each case *Dasein* is always '*ahead* of itself' in its being. *Dasein* is always 'beyond itself,' not relative to other be-ings which it is *not,* but as being toward the being-able-to-be which it is itself."[145] Because of this leeway, several possibilities are open to man. At every moment he has the possibility to be other than he is now. In principle, man is always other than he actually is now. He is always a project, a project-in-the-world, because his being is a being-in-the-world. To every possibility which man's own being can take up there corresponds a possible meaning of the world. Thus, the project which man himself is, is equi-primordially the project of his world. In his own

---

[142] Heidegger, *Sein und Zeit,* pp. 41-45 (English ed., pp. 67-71).
[143] Luijpen, *art. cit.* in footnote 140, p. 616.
[144] Heidegger, *op. cit.,* p. 145 (English ed., p. 185).
[145] Heidegger, *ibid.,* pp. 191-192 (English ed., p. 236).

being man is always concerned with his own possibilities, but at the same time also with the possibilities of the world.[146]

Man's ability to be is, as we have said, always an ability within a determined factical situation. Facticity and situation always bind and limit me on all sides. My freedom must always begin with the bonds of my situation. For this reason the project which I am is a "thrown" project. "And as thrown, *Dasein* is thrown into the mode of being called 'projecting.' "[147] My facticity is no real facticity without the leeway of my ability to be, but on the other hand, this being-able-to-be is not a real possibility save from the starting point of my facticity.

---

[146] Luijpen, *art. cit.* in footnote 140, pp. 614-618.
[147] Same reference as footnote 145, p. 145 (Eng. ed. 185).

CHAPTER FOUR

PHILOSOPHY AND SCIENCE

In this chapter we will try to determine the proper characters of philosophy and of the sciences, basing ourselves on the above-described view of intentionality. For a good understanding of the problem, it will be necessary to start with a few brief historical considerations regarding the theory of science.

1. Historical Considerations of the Theory of Science

The Ancient and Medieval Period. From the time of Plato, man has had to face the fact that his knowledge develops in more than one dimension. The problems to which this fact gave rise were at first concerned only with the description and definition of these dimensions. It was not very long before different views regarding these matters manifested themselves. Ancient and scholastic philosophy knew two entirely different types of division of the sciences, viz., the Platonic and the Aristotelian divisions.

By the Platonic division we mean the division into physics, ethics, and dialectics. It was first attributed to Plato by Cicero, although it is not quite certain that Plato himself made this division. The Platonic division was taken over by the Stoics, the Epicurians, by numerous ancient pagan and Christian writers, such as St. Augustine, and by a very large number of medieval thinkers of Mohammedan, Jewish, and Christian backgrounds.

The Aristotelian division, which is based mainly on Aristotle's *Metaphysics,* divides the sciences into practical and theoretical disciplines. The theoretical sciences are then further subdivided into physics, mathematics, and metaphysics. In addition to the speculative and practical sciences this division admitted logical, grammatical, and rhetorical disciplines, which did not form part of the system of sciences in the proper sense. This division was taken over in a largely unanimous fashion by those who sought their inspiration in Aristotle's philosophy.

At the beginning of the thirteenth century, the Aristotelian division gradually managed to replace the Platonic division in a definitive way.[148] It continued to be the generally accepted division until the sixteenth century, when "Modern Philosophy" caused it to be largely abandoned. However, even today there are philosophers who try to maintain the Aristotelian division with more or less essential modifications.

The point that interests us most in these first attempted systematizations of the sciences is the fact that the large majority of these ancient thinkers did not see the problem involved in the unity and plurality of science. As we have mentioned, at a very early date it was noted that the unity of man's knowing developed into a plurality of dimensions. Although this fact did not fail to raise problems, these questions served only as starting points of speculations regarding the division and systematization of the sciences. The question, as we know it now, about the unity and diversity of science never became a serious and urgent problem. The reason lies perhaps in the fact that all sciences were viewed as philosophical and, therefore, as obviously unified in dialectics or metaphysics as "first philosophy."

The Modern Period. When the fifteenth and sixteenth centuries laid the foundations of what later would become modern physical science, it became increasingly apparent that the Aristotelian division of the sciences was not acceptable. The old division was unable to assign a suitable place in its system to the new science; moreover, many thinkers began to view philosophy and science in a quite different fashion. Since that time there have been numerous attempts to determine accurately the nature of philosophy and that of science, to find their mutual relationship, and to discover a suitable systematic division. From the sixteenth century on, moreover, there have been many explicit pleas for the unity of the sciences. It suffices to mention in this connection the considerations of Francis Bacon, Descartes, Leibniz, d'Alembert, Diderot, Kant, Fichte, Hegel, Comte, Marx, and others.

This problem concerning the unity of science, which arose with the sixteenth century birth of physical science, became even more urgent later when several "mental sciences" began to develop and when physical

---

[148] Cf. A. Mansion, *Introduction à la physique artistotélicienne,* Paris, 1945; A. Mariétan, *Problème de la classification des sciences,* Paris, 1901; Kockelmans, "De betekenis van de term 'materia intelligibilis' in de werken van St. Thomas," *Tijdschrift voor Philosophie,* vol. 15 (1953), pp. 71-86 and the literature quoted there.

science itself, losing the homogeneous character which it had hitherto enjoyed, split into an increasing number of heterogeneous disciplines. True, at first many thinkers were convinced that even the mental sciences would be able to flourish only if they took over the methods of the physical sciences. However, efforts to do so were only partially successful, for it became increasingly clear that, through this "physicalization," these sciences would never be able to discover their own character. Thus, by the beginning of the twentieth century, the development of science was accompanied by an ever greater specialization and divergence of objects and methods, giving rise to an ever increasing number of relatively autonomous sciences.

Many viewed this situation as alarming because the "unity of our view of reality" seems to be placed in jeopardy. Some argued that the primary role of philosophy consists in co-ordinating the results of the various partial sciences, so that in this way the unity of the world view could still be saved. Others, however, continued to claim that philosophy is essentially distinct from the other sciences and therefore had to seek another solution of the problem. Since none of the proposed solutions really satisfied anyone, a few began to speak about a crisis in the sciences. The question was asked whether, despite all the leaps and bounds of progress achieved by the various sciences, man was really on the right track.[149]

Before we can evaluate the issue, it will be necessary to formulate the problem more sharply and to present it with more details. We will do that in the following section of this chapter.

2. Scientism

The Roots of Scientism. In 1936 Husserl published the first volume of his work, *Die Krisis der europäischen Wissenschaften.* In this book he also sees the root of the crisis affecting modern science in the conceptions of science which arose in the sixteenth century on the occasion of the birth of the new physical science. For, physical science, which made increasingly more use of mathematics as its method, managed to make rapid progress in a short time and thus cast a shadow

---

[149] Concerning this matter see Husserl, *Die Krisis . . . , passim;* W. Gerlach, E. Grassi, T. von Uexküll, G. Bally and W. Szilasi, *Die Einheit unseres Wirklichkeitsbildes und die Grenzen der Einzelwissenschaften,* München, 1951; A. Dempf, *Die Einheit der Wissenschaft,* Stuttgart, 1955.

over philosophy. Gradually the idea arose that it should be possible to introduce the method of physical science, in other words, mathematics, into all other sciences. In this way, moreover, the various sciences together with philosophy would be able to constitute a single all-encompassing total science. The idea was "that the infinite totality of all be-ings forms a rational all-encompassing unity, which therefore could be dominated by one corresponding universal science, and this in such a way that nothing would be left over."[150] According to Husserl, Descartes was the first thinker who managed to develop this view into a consistent system.

During the next three hundred years a large group of thinkers endeavored to determine this ideal in a more concrete fashion. Around the middle of the nineteenth century the following view, which Renouvier very aptly called "scientism," was rather commonly accepted. There is no other possibility of knowledge than that used by physical science. There exists no other reality than that which is disclosed by physics and the sciences using the methods of physics. The purpose of philosophy is not so much to study whatever transcends the perceptible world as to systematize the various sciences into a single well-ordered whole.

Opposition to this view arose on all sides, including that of the physicists and especially of those who devoted themselves to the so-called "critique of the sciences."[151] We will see more about this critique after we have indicated the viewpoint of scientism in more detail.

Characteristics of Scientism. In general, one can say that the following ideas are typical of scientism. The fundamental assumption is that there exists a single, infinite and rational totality of being, which can be fully known in a fully rational way by a single science by means of a single method. In other words, there is only one objective world, which in principle is accessible to anyone and can be known in an objective way, as it really is, through a single science.

When, in that science, an effort is made to conquer this totality of being rationally the first task is to choose as the starting point that which is immediately evident. Such evidence can be obtained only by dividing the object of research into the smallest possible parts, in accordance with Francis Bacon's rule: *dissecare naturam* (to divide nature). Knowledge

---

[150] Husserl, *Die Krisis* . . . , pp. 18-20.
[151] F. Sassen and B. Delfgaauw, *Wijsbegeerte van onze tijd,* pp. 361-372; Luijpen, *op. cit.,* pp. 15-16 and 89.

of more complex things has to be logically developed from the elements gathered by knowledge of the more simple.

According to this view, only that is objective which can be determined by certain principles, namely, the principles based on quantity. Hence, the boundaries of sciences lie where this objective approach can no longer be used. That which is not quantitative is, consequently, not objective and therefore is also meaningless. According to the well-known statement of Keppler, it is only as quantity or through quantity that man's knowledge reaches perfection.

The objective realm with which science is concerned is not the domain of the senses, for a fundamental distinction has to be made between primary and secondary qualities. Only the primary qualities deserve to be called objective. The secondary qualities have only a subjective value and, as such, are unimportant for science. This idea harmonizes with the thesis of Democritus, the Father of mechanism: "Sweet and bitter, cold and warm, as also colors, all this exists only in our opinion but not really."[152]

Although for Descartes himself experience played only a very minor role,[153] the sciences rather quickly returned to Aristotle's ideal that all science must begin with experience. However, if the fundamental rule of all science is that it must start with experience, and if only the quantitative or mathematical aspect is objective, and, finally, if only the primary qualities are objectively meaningful, then it follows that the experience in question can consist of nothing other than counting or measuring. As Hassenstein expressed it quite recently, that which cannot be discovered by counting or measuring has no value for science: "Everything else is merely 'subjective' and, as such, only appearance and deception."[154]

If a distinction is made between primary and secondary qualities and only the former are considered endowed with objectivity, one reduces the most obvious view of the world to a more hidden view which, however, is supposed to be endowed with greater rationality and more evidence. In other words, the world as it presents itself immediately to man

[152] Quoted by H. Weyl, "Wissenschaft als symbolische Konstruktion des Menschen," *Eranos Jahrbuch,* vol. 16, p. 375.

[153] J. Maréchal, *Le point de départ de la métaphysique,* Paris, 1944-49, vol. 2, pp. 51-61.

[154] Quoted by T. von Uexküll, "Die Einheit der Naturwissenschaften," *op. cit.* in footnote 149, p. 95. Cf. also H. van de Hulst and C. van Peursen, *Phaenomenologie en natuurwetenschap,* Utrecht, 1953, pp. 20-31.

conceals another world that is more essential. This hidden world lies behind the world of everyday experience, which is merely a world of appearances.

The elimination of man himself from the scientific world is connected with these ideas. On the one hand, the secondary sensible qualities are wholly attributed to man and, being subjective properties, they are, as it were, taken out of the world and placed in man himself. On the other hand, the primary qualities are detached from man and wholly ascribed to the external world. These latter phenomena are of interest to science; it studies a world free from man's subjective admixtures. As G. Bally correctly remarks, the man of science, therefore, may ask only questions "which can be answered by the naming of quantitative differences. But this implies that he himself may be present only insofar as he makes comparisons by measurement. This reduction of the subjective being to a circumscribed and exact function, which runs its course in the same way in all other subjects, makes it possible to neglect the part of the subject in the scientific encounter and to concentrate attention on the objects and events perceived by measuring observation."[155]

Scientism, moreover, assumes a principle of determinism,[156] i.e., from the quantitative description of an existing situation and from the known laws governing the changes of the magnitudes involved in the situation, a univocal prediction can be made regarding the changes occurring in the situation in question. If the expectation is not fulfilled or fully fulfilled, then either our measurements of the situation were not exact or the laws allowing us to calculate the changes were not sufficiently accurate.

Apart from measuring observation and statistics, only the deductive method is considered to be valid. Mathematics is the model and core of such a deductive reasoning process. Adherents of scientism are not interested in, or appreciative of, analytic procedures such as those often used in philosophy. Whatever is discovered in the various partial domains of the totality of being studied by the particular sciences has to be reducible to a few general laws; reversely, whatever we experience through measurement must be deducible from these laws.[157]

A major driving force behind all this scientific activity is the desire to control the world technically. One of its basic questions is, and always

---

[155] G. Bally, "Biologie und Psychologie," *op. cit.* in footnote 149, p. 115.
[156] W. Gerlach, "Die Grenzen der physikalischen Erkenntnis," *ibid.,* p. 48.
[157] von Uexküll, *op. cit.,* pp. 94-95.

has been, the question of "what one can do with the objects."[158] There are, however, other motives, among which theoretical interest has to be mentioned explicitly.[159]

3. Scientism and Psychology

The Introduction of Scientism into Psychology. As we have mentioned, this view of science, which was partially sustained by the hope of preserving the unity of science, was at first very successful.[160] It led to significant results, first of all, in the empirical sciences of nature, especially in physics and chemistry, but later also in the biological and psychological sciences, and ultimately, to a certain extent, even in philosophy. As a clear illustration of the situation resulting from the uncontrolled and uncritical application of the fundamental principles and methods of physical science to other domains we may refer to the case of psychology.

Empirical psychology was one of the first sciences to follow the trail blazed by physical science. The oldest psychological schools were psychologies based on the principles of physical science. For example, the psychology of association, in imitation of physical science, sought its salvation in analysis, i.e., it tried to obtain knowledge of the ultimate elements which, in accordance with fixed laws, were supposed to combine into higher complexes. Moreover, like physical science, it wanted to provide causal explanations by causally connecting psychical events with physical stimuli and physiological processes.

Johann Herbart, moreover, explicitly connected this physical psychology with mathematics. He began to measure psychical phenomena and to establish functional relations between the resulting numbers. Hermann von Helmholz introduced the experiment into psychology, thereby bringing this science, methodically speaking, completely in line with physics and chemistry.

It would be interesting to follow the historical development of this

---

[158] Bally, *op. cit.*, pp. 113-114.

[159] Concerning this whole matter see Husserl, *Die Krisis . . .* , pp. 18-60; Merleau-Ponty, *Phenomenology of Perception,* pp. 3-153 (especially pp. 6-12, 23-31, 54-57, 59-63, 70-80, 101-106, 137-143; van de Hulst and van Peursen, *op. cit.,* pp. 7-31; F. Buytendijk, "Vernieuwing in de wetenschap," *Annalen v.h. Thijmgenootschap,* vol. 42, pp. 230-247; R. Kwant and J. van den Berk, "Het gesprek van de physicus met de wereld," *ibid.,* vol. 43, pp. 1-19; Kwant, "Het phenomenologisch wetenschapsideaal," *Tijdschrift voor zielkunde en opvoedingsleer,* vol. 27, pp. 20-34.

[160] von Uexküll, *op. cit.,* pp. 94-95.

aspect of psychology unto the present day and to dwell upon the ideas of Wilhelm Wundt and especially of such behaviorists as Ivan P. Pavlov, Edward Lee Thorndike, and John B. Watson. It would show us how, in spite of all improvements and new ideas, a large part of that physicalistic psychology managed to maintain itself. However, we will restrict ourselves to indicating in what exactly this physicalistic psychology of around 1900 consisted.

Characteristics of Scientistic Psychology Around 1900. First of all, the old psychology was an elemental psychology. It endeavored to reduce all complex psychical phenomena to ultimate psychical elements and subsequently to synthetize the higher complexes from those elements. In other words, its ideal was a kind of mental chemistry. It studied all phenomena as separately from one another as possible and believed that it could understand man's psychical life in its living complexity by connecting the separately studied elements.

Secondly, the psychical elements having been discovered, the old psychology sought the general laws according to which those elements are joined to constitute complex psychical phenomena. Just as physical science tends to find the laws governing physical processes, so this psychology sought to discover the general laws ruling the course of psychical events. These laws were supposed to be the blindly operating mechanical laws of association and to be the same for all individuals.

Moreover, it was assumed that man's entire psychical life was causally determined. As in physics and chemistry, all events in the realm of psychology, supposedly, were controlled by the law of cause and effect. All conscious processes, it was held, ran their course in a rigorously causal and mechanical fashion, so that man was hardly more than an exceedingly complicated machine. The ultimate cause of all psychical phenomena was sought in physical stimuli and physiological processes. As a consequence, like physical science, that kind of psychology attempted to explain the psychical phenomena without any value judgments. It viewed man simply as a datum of nature, subject to blind iron-clad laws of nature and fully determined by those laws.

Furthermore, the psychology of around 1900 endeavored to study the phenomena of consciousness as independent units divorced from the *I*. It did not admit any difference in this respect between those phenomena and the objects or things of inorganic nature. Consequently, it viewed the soul as a collection of elements of consciousness, dependent only on stimuli from the external world or from certain nervous processes. In other words, the soul did not take any active part in these phenomena but played only a passive role.

Finally, that psychology thought that the exact method of physical science could be applied to an object which is quite different from that of physical science. It assumed also that there could be question of measurability in the realm of psychology. Mathematical equations were highly regarded and it was thought possible to fix the most complex psychical phenomena in terms of measures, numbers and laws. Great importance was attached, for instance, to the measurement of reaction times, the calculus of correlations, and the application of statistical methods.

To sum up, the driving force of classical, objectifying psychology was to study experiences and behavior as if they were things, quantifiable and measurable magnitudes, subject to investigation of their causal relationships. For this reason everything psychical was reduced to thinglike elements and studied as processes, in imitation of the physical sciences.[161]

4. The Crisis of the Scientistic View

Similar remarks could be made with respect to other sciences, such as biology, medicine, and sociology. Here also the application of the method proper to physical science at first produced valuable results. In the course of time, however, serious difficulties arose in all these realms, and these difficulties gradually revealed themselves to be fundamental.

Biology. In biology, for example, it became evident that the wealth of the biological phenomenon exceeded the possibilities of quantitative considerations and that physical and chemical studies of the biological object, strictly speaking, do not touch the biological as such. The object of biology, that which biology can objectively know, revealed itself to encompass much more than quantitative aspects. It appeared to be a prejudice to hold fast to the idea that in biology only the mathematically causal aspect can be an object of consideration. Thus, it appeared no longer feasible to call the non-quantitative aspects of living organisms subjective, illusory, or imaginary. It became gradually evident that what is objective in biology is even essentially distinct from the

---

[161] G. Bally, *op. cit.* in footnote 155, pp. 107-127; B. Kouwer and J. Linschoten, *Inleiding tot de psychologie,* Assen, 1953, pp. 17-57; Ph. Kohnstamm, J. Linschoten, M. Langeveld, B. Kouwer, D. van Lennep, and B. Palland, *Inleiding in de psychologie,* Groningen, 1955, pp. 331-354.

measurable objectivity pursued by physical science. Biologically speaking, the physical aspect is neither meaningful nor meaningless but simply without meaning; for the biologist it is totally different. A quantitative study, strictly speaking, does not concern itself with the proper object of biology. The physical aspect becomes meaningful in biology only after it has been methodically integrated with, and subordinated to the living.[162]

Psychology. A similar situation soon arose in psychology. For Christian von Wolff, who introduced psychology as a science, psychology was identical with psychometry and it retained this status throughout its positivistic period. Toward the beginning of our century, however, difficulties made themselves felt. They revealed in essence that the strictly psychological aspect cannot be approached by means of a physical method. It is sufficient to name in this context the investigations of depth psychology, Gestalt psychology, structure psychology, personalistic and phenomenological psychology, and the various other trends which have arisen since 1900. Despite the diversity present in these psychological currents, one can indicate a general characteristic in them, viz., the rejection of the physical method and the attempt to discover a proper "psychological experience" independent of all measurement. All now appear convinced that a psychology patterned on physical science is impossible, although, on the other hand, no one wants to deny the important contributions made by the "physical methods" in connection with the study of the objects of psychology and biology.[163]

Physical Science. In physical science itself the physical method has been largely maintained until the present, but even there problems have arisen which throw an entirely new light on the meaning of this method. One of the most characteristic features in this matter is that modern physical science realizes that it does not speak about "objective" things but about the knowledge which we have of these things and their behavior. Man is no longer a "disinterested" onlooker in physical science but he plays a role. The object of physical science is not "nature in itself" but "nature as questioned by man," so that the investigating thinker also encounters himself in his study. The object of physical science appears to be the network of relationships between nature and man. As C. von Weizsäcker correctly writes, "Perhaps the most important contribution of contemporary physical science lies in the fact

---

[162] A. Portmann, "Über die Eigenart des biologischen Forschens," *op. cit.* in footnote 149, pp. 69-93.
[163] See the references of footnote 161.

that it points out that it is necessary to conceive the relationship of matter and consciousness, of object and subject, differently from the way it has been done in the philosophical tradition of the past centuries."[164]

The Reason for the Changed Mentality. It is not easy to determine exactly and fully why this change of mentality has come about. Nevertheless, several factors can be named that have contributed to this change. First of all, there is the fact that in any measurement the subject cannot be fully eliminated, for it always remains necessary to observe sensitively a spatio-temporal co-incidence of factors. Undoubtedly also, Heisenberg's uncertainty relations have exercised a certain influence on the change of mentality.

There is more, however. In the past decades the topic has been discussed repeatedly, implicitly and explicitly, in connection with the relationship between theory and experiment. Theory and experiment are now viewed as essentially connected. An experiment is called scientific only if it is guided by a theory; reversely, a scientific hypothesis becomes a theory only when it is confirmed by scientific experience. An experience is an experience only when the observer is guided by a theory, but a theory, on the other hand, is meaningful only when experience gives it validity. If this is true, then it is evident that the proper object of physical science is not nature taken in itself but nature as viewed by the physicist. Hence the part of the subject cannot be fully eliminated in the physical observation. As a consequence, the physical world view is neither objective nor absolute in the sense of Descartes.

Moreover, the ideal of a single, all-embracing science cannot be maintained even for the domain of inorganic nature. For, if the role of the subject cannot be fully eliminated in the scientific observation, then the starting point of the physical sciences is not univocal. It follows therefore that there exists a possibility that even the edifice of physical science will disintegrate into several relatively autonomous parts.[165]

---

[164] C. von Weiszäcker and J. Juilfs, *Physik der Gegenwart,* Bonn, 1953, p. 11; W. Heisenberg, *Das Naturbild der heutigen Physik,* Hamburg, 1957, pp. 11-12, 18, 21. Concerning this whole matter see also F. Buytendijk, *art. cit.,* pp. 239-241; van de Hulst and van Peursen, *op. cit.,* pp. 50-94; Dondeyne, "Idealisme of realisme?" *Tijdschrift voor Philosophie,* vol. 3, pp. 623-24 and 647.

[165] S. Gagnebin, "Théorie et expérience. Le problème," *Dialectica,* vol. 6, pp. 120-129; G. Isaye, "Expérience et théorie. Les troisièmes entretiens de Zürich," *Revue philosophique de Louvain,* vol. 49, pp. 446-461; J. Clay, "Le rapport entre l'expérience et la théorie," *Dialectica,* vol. 6, pp. 266-269; J. Rossel, "Théorie et expérience, *ibid.,* pp. 260-263; J. Ladrière, "Concepts scientifiques et idées

5. *Phenomenology and Scientism*

Rejection of the Claims of Scientism. Summarizing, we may say that since the time of Descartes it had been assumed that, by means of mathematics, it should be possible to construct a single, all-embracing and rational science covering all sciences and even philosophy itself. We have seen in what way the proponents of this ideal described and defined the science in question, how the new physical science began to flourish through the use of this method, how the other sciences, influenced by the enormous success of physics, took over its method and reneged their own character in the course of their progressive physicalization. Finally, we have seen how resistance arose in the various sciences against this betrayal of their proper nature and how each of them gradually learned to find its own object and method without, however, entirely escaping the influence of physical science.

We must now ask ourselves how we have to evaluate all this from the standpoint of phenomenology. This evaluation may be briefly expressed in the following way. In harmony with the movement that has been growing in the various sciences during the past few decades, phenomenology also rejects the claims of the Cartesian unitary science. Phenomenologists, too, consider it incorrect to claim that there is only one way of speaking about reality, viz., the way of the physical sciences, and, correspondingly, that only the world of physical science can aspire to objectivity. Moreover, it is not true that only measurement and experiment constitute real and objective experience and that natural and spontaneous experience can have only a subjective value. Phenomenology also rejects the idea that only the "clear and distinct ideas of quantity" are objective and that secondary qualities have only a subjective value.

The Faulty Foundation of Scientism. Phenomenology sees the root of all these faulty ideas in the *a priori* assumption that knowledge is a pure mirroring of a world-in-itself that exists independently of man. For, it is only against the background of this fundamental mistake that one could substitute for man's original experience the experience of

---

philosophiques," *La relativité de notre connaissance,* by L. de Raeymaeker, W. Mund and J. Ladrière, Louvain, 1948, pp. 103-156; M. Altwegg, "Theorie und Erfahrung," *Dialectica,* vol. 7, pp. 5-21; H. Weyl, *Philosophy of Mathematics and Natural Science,* Princeton, 1949, pp. 139-164.

physical science and that the objective world of this science could be put into the place of the original world in which man lives.[166]

Thus, according to phenomenology, that faulty conception starts with the assumption that man is in a world in which he can let his mind freely roam, a world he can consider in any part without thereby changing the "objective" nature of the considered reality. That view assumes, moreover, that, corresponding to this one objective world, there is a single absolute observer. He is able to unite all the different stand-points, from which we must always look at things, into a single all-encompassing total view and merge all the perspectives experienced by us into a single objective whole. The entire ideal of the above-described "unitary science" was at first based on the opposition between an autonomously existing spatial and temporal world and the consciousness facing this world. This opposition was formulated with all desirable clarity in Descartes' distinction between "extended thing" and "thinking thing" (*res extensa* and *res cogitans*).[167]

Consciousness and World. According to that view, the object pole is an objectively existing world which can be fully explained and exactly expressed in objective laws. This objective world exists wholly in itself and possesses a rationality that can be fully understood. The subject, on the other hand, is pure consciousness, an interiority divorced from the world, transparent to itself, and facing the perfectly rational world that is open to its understanding.[168] This view was explicitly or implicitly accepted by practically all the above-mentioned men of science, although not all of them interpreted it in the same way. In the realistic interpretation of this fundamental view, meaning is found in the world itself as existing in itself, wholly independently of man, while, in the idealistic interpretation, meaning lies in a consciousness that is divorced from the world.

For phenomenologists, however, the world of experience from which every science proceeds is not independent of man. They unanimously reject the objectively pre-given world and the general spectator for whom this objective world would lie open as a landscape lies before the gaze of a tourist. All knowledge and all science begin in a perception

---

[166] Merleau-Ponty, *Sens et Non-Sens,* p. 185; *Phenomenology of Perception,* pp. 71 ff.

[167] Heisenberg, *op. cit.,* p. 21; Buytendijk, *art. cit.,* pp. 237, 239-241.

[168] Merleau-Ponty, *Phenomenology of Perception,* pp. 207 f.; Kwant and van den Berk, *art. cit.* in footnote 159, pp. 2-3.

which is essentially co-existence and communication of man and the world;[169] they do not begin in an openness toward a kind of intrinsically immutable world-in-itself which would remain unaffected by this perception. All human knowledge of the world is ultimately knowledge of a human world; there exists no other world.[170] For this reason our knowledge and science of the world cannot consist of letting our gaze roam over this world as over something that is external to this gaze. Phenomenologists cannot conceive the world *a priori* as a whole whose various parts can be isolated and analyzed without being thereby modified.[171]

For phenomenology the essence of the crisis which the sciences face today, without perhaps being clearly aware of it, lies in the fact that it has become impossible to make a sharp distinction between a world existing in itself and, on the other hand, a consciousness facing this world, a consciousness which would be able to know this objective world in an objective way as it is in itself. The distinction between subjective and objective possesses only a limited value and is variable within the framework of the various forms of human existence.[172]

A Plurality of Worlds. The reason why phenomenology holds this position is that man is never without a world, he always finds himself in a world and can be known only from this world. Through his bodily being, perception, action, thinking and ability, man is situated in this world. All this supplies him with knowledge, and through this many-sided knowing and the direction which his knowledge takes each man forms the world in which he dwells. Hence there is a plurality of worlds, but there is for everyone, originally, a common everyday world, which invites him to take a certain standpoint and to form a system of meanings. Man's choice of his world-project is at the same time the choice of his mode of being and determines the subjectivity and objectivity which he will encounter there.

On the basis of this view concerning human existence, phenomenology presents a different evaluation of the sciences. The former idea of a single objective, absolute and autonomous real world implied that every science should occupy itself with a part of reality; the man of science

---

[169] Merleau-Ponty, *op. cit.,* p. 213.

[170] Merleau-Ponty, *ibid.,* pp. 431 f. Concerning this statement see also our article quoted in footnote 123.

[171] de Waelhens, *Une philosophie de l'ambiguïté. L'existentialisme de Maurice Merleau-Ponty,* Louvain, 1951, p. 388.

[172] Buytendijk, *art. cit.,* p. 237.

should try to penetrate as profoundly as possible into that partial realm in order to give the greatest possible increase to his knowledge. Now it is realized, however, that scientific knowledge is controlled by the way in which the man of science projects his field of study. Every science has its own "world."[173]

Knowledge as Encounter Between Man and World. Phenomenology views human knowledge in general as an encounter between man and the world, in which neither one nor the other is wholly passive or wholly active. The subject does not receive an objectively existing world in a purely passive fashion, but every act of perception and therefore any subsequent act of knowledge bears the seal of both partners, of the world and of man. Hence man's knowledge cannot be considered as a gaze that passively accepts a given meaning nor as the act of a pure spirit which in a wholly active way creates meaning from within. Our knowledge, therefore, is not a mirroring of a pre-given meaning, as positivism maintains, nor the immanent development of a meaning, as rationalism claims, but the unfolding of meaning in an encounter of man with the world. And in this encounter there always arises a certain field of meaning.[174]

The dialogue in question manifests itself to be different in every concrete case, to demand a different method in every case, and to lead to a different form of objectivity in every case. For this reason every science has its own conception of objectivity. There is no longer only one objective world, but there appear to be many "worlds," which are neither more nor less objective than the world projected, for example, by physical science. These scientific "worlds" are determined by the way in which the men of each science project their field of study in the experiences that constitute their starting point. Thus, the proper field of the various sciences is a certain realm of meaning, which is constituted by a certain way of encounter with the world and which therefore demands a method of its own.

In this view of the sciences it is no longer to be expected that the results of the various branches of knowledge will constitute a homogeneous unity. On the contrary, the more the sciences become specialized, the more the field of meaning proper to each science will assume an

---

[173] Buytendijk, *ibid.,* pp. 237-238; Heidegger, *Sein und Zeit,* pp. 363, 393 (English ed., pp. 414, 445).

[174] Kwant and van den Berk, *art. cit.* in footnote 159, p. 2.

irreducible character. Hence, one who abandons the illusion that the sciences are an objective mirroring of a world-in-itself, also gives up hope that the results attained by the different sciences will merge into a single objective synthesis. On the other hand, phenomenology does not deny every bond between the different sciences. However, it does not seek their unity in the synthesis of their ultimate results, but in their common root and starting point, the original experience and the field of presence originally constituted in that experience.[175]

In the following pages we will develop the positive aspects of this phenomenological viewpoint.

6. The Essential Distinction Between Science and Philosophy

Radical Thinking. For the phenomenologist there is an essential distinction between science and philosophy. A fundamental difference lies in the fact that the sciences do not think radically while, on the other hand, radical, presuppositionless thinking is characteristic of philosophy. Because of this essential difference in thinking, which implies at the same time a far-reaching difference of method, there is an unbridgeable abyss between philosophy and science. Any conceivable transition meets with insuperable difficulties because there is no bridge connecting the two. In other words, one who wants to switch from philosophy to science, or vice versa, can do so only by "leaping," by an abrupt change of attitude.[176]

The Inability of Science to Explain the Essence of Its Own Realm of Research. When philosophers make such a statement, scientists are likely to view that assertion as derogatory of science, but that is not at all what the philosopher intends. Philosophy does not want to speak against science, but act on behalf of it. For, science wants to obtain clarity concerning its own essence but is itself unable to reach this purpose. Another feature which strikes anyone who studies the essence of science is, indeed, the fact that science is unable to devote its attention to the essence of its own realm of research. The historian, for instance, using purely historical means, will never discover the proper nature of the

---

[175] Kwant, "Het phenomenologisch wetenschapsideaal," *Tijdschrift voor Zielkunde en Opvoedingsleer,* vol. 27, pp. 35-39; Kwant and van den Berk, *art. cit.,* pp. 2-3.

[176] Heidegger, *Was heisst Denken?* Tübingen, 1954, pp. 4-5.

historical; the mathematician, using purely mathematical means, can never explain what the essence of the mathematical is. The proper nature of the domain of its object is hidden from any particular science. It is the task of philosophy to ask questions concerning this nature and to attempt to clarify the issue. Precisely because science reveals itself deprived of access to the essence of the domain constituting its object, we must say that science is unable to think radically.

At first sight it may seem that philosophy exhibits also here a higher opinion of itself than of scientific thought. However, it should be kept in mind that philosophy is not unaware that it has not yet succeeded in discovering the essence of the mathematical, of nature, or of the historical and that, in this matter therefore, it knows, strictly speaking, even less than the sciences. The latter, in the course of centuries, have gained every right to their name because, within the limits laid down for them, they have attained great results. Nevertheless, it is and remains true that the sciences are one-sided in the sense that they cannot reflect on the essence of the objects which they consider, at least as long as they remain faithful to their own scientific character. The marvelous results which they have achieved within their own realm often make the sciences forget this one-sidedness and lead them to appropriate to themselves the rights of philosophy. That kind of "positivism," however, is wholly unacceptable since philosophy and science do not lie in the same line.[177]

Presuppositions. A third point of attention in a study of the issue concerning the essence of the sciences is the fact that the sciences always start from presuppositions which they themselves cannot provide with a scientific foundation. Philosophy, on the other hand, never bases itself on the data established by history, mathematics, or physical science, nor on any other presuppositions, but is really a "science based on the ultimate foundation."[178]

A final characteristic of contemporary science is that, for the sciences, whatever is appears only in that objectivity which is constituted and maintained by the different scientific objectivations.[179] Since this point demands to be explained more extensively, we will devote the following pages to it. At the same time we will have an opportunity to clarify and substantiate the other three assertions regarding the essence of science.

---

[177] Heidegger, *ibid.,* pp. 49, 56-58.

[178] Heidegger, *ibid.,* p. 90; Husserl, "Philosophie als strenge Wissenschaft," *Logos,* vol. 1, p. 340.

[179] Heidegger, *ibid.,* pp. 155-156.

7. Scientific Objectivation

The Beginning of All Scientific Investigation. As we have seen above, for phenomenology intentionality, as the root and origin of all meaning, indicates primarily not a cognitive relationship but a relationship of being. In this idea of intentionality knowledge merely refers to a special mode of our being-in-the-world. The characteristic feature of this mode is that man limits himself to observing the world without being totally involved in it. This contemplative gaze already contains a certain attitude toward worldly be-ings and, correlatively, that which is encountered in this way is always viewed from a certain standpoint. Which aspect the world will reveal to man's theoretical gaze depends on his attitude toward be-ings. By taking such an aspect as the object of a critical and methodic inquiry, he lays the foundation for a particular science.

Accordingly, the man of science, through his attitude with respect to what presents itself, begins by determining a domain of the world as his realm of investigation. The opening-up and careful demarcation of a well-circumscribed realm appears to be the beginning of all scientific investigation. That the object of every science constitutes a well-defined realm is manifest from the fact that this object *a priori* prescribes what questions or problems may be asked. Every new phenomenon manifesting itself in such a realm is questioned as long as it fits in with the normative objective interconnection of the science in question.[180]

Thematization. The question, however, is how is such an objective realm opened up and demarcated? According to phenomenology, in any theoretical orientation to the world, and certainly in any scientific orientation, the scientific experience already contains a certain thematization in which the object of knowledge is originally thematized, constituted, and projected.[181] In this project a certain realm of be-ings is circumscribed, the approach to this realm receives its particular methodic direction, the structure of conceptual and discursive explanation is given its orientation, and a special "language" is constituted. The thematiza-

---

[180] Heidegger, "Die Zeit des Weltbildes," *Holzwege,* Frankfurt a.M., 1957, pp. 56-58.
[181] Heidegger, *Sein und Zeit,* p. 363 (English ed., p. 414); Merleau-Ponty, *Phenomenology of Perception,* pp. 241-242.

tion, then, encompasses that original project, the demarcation of a certain objective realm, the determination of the method of approach to this realm, and the orientation of the conceptual structure and linguistic forms of expression relevant to this realm.   Hence the intention of the thematization is to disengage a worldly be-ing or a group of be-ings in such a way that they can thereby become the object of a purely theoretical disclosure and thus can be questioned "objectively."

Phenomenology, then, demands that every science be "objective" in the sense that it adheres to the facts, but it refuses to accept that those facts can be dehumanized, as positivism claims, or that they have to be divorced from the world, as rationalism maintains.   Its reason for taking this position is that the scientific subject is also a being-in-the-world and therefore continues to be at least partially involved in the world.[182]

Clarifying the position of phenomenology, Heidegger makes a distinction between the "readiness-to-hand" (*Zuhandenheit*) of things in our daily "concern" (*Besorgen*) and the "presence-at-hand" (*Vorhandenheit*) of the same things in our scientific attitude.   He argues that just as our daily "concern" precedes our scientific consideration, so also "readiness-to-hand" precedes "presence-at-hand."   Before we are able to conceive a thing under a certain aspect in a limiting and abstracting consideration, we must have had this thing before us in an all-encompassing attitude of total involvement.   Hence the change of standpoint proper to the theoretical man has a limiting and abstracting function which breaks the original datum into many parts so that a single aspect can be sharply illuminated.

For this reason, even with respect to its scientific experience itself, every science is rooted in the *a priori* of the formality under which the thing is going to be considered.   Everything else depends on this *a priori* formality: the foundations of the investigation, the method, the "language," the type of demonstration, the mode of intelligibility, the view of truth and certainty.   Every science, therefore, is rooted in a way of making a worldly be-ing present that differs from the way of being present in our daily "concern" and pays attention only to the objective discovery of a be-ing as purely given for this theoretical consideration. It considers that be-ing as "purely present-at-hand" (*rein Vorhanden-den*).[183]

---

[182] Heidegger, *ibid.*, pp. 59-62, 363 (English ed., pp. 85-90, 414).

[183] Heidegger, *ibid.*, pp. 153-160, 356-364 (English ed., pp. 194-203, 408-415); de Waelhens, *La philosophie de Martin Heidegger,* Louvain, 1955, pp. 40-49, 87-98, 197-205.

The Abstract Character of the Object of Science. Accordingly, the ultimate material object of science is perceived reality and its task is to describe what it has perceived as "present-at-hand," i.e., from the standpoint of an ontic objectivation.[184] Hence it follows not only that science is abstract in itself but also that its proper object must always be something abstract. For reality as "presence-at-hand" is merely the correlate of a secondary intentionality, based upon and starting from our original intention which is essentially co-existence. If, then, in science we speak of reality as object in itself, we are at once concerned with reality only in a dimension which is merely virtually included in our perception but with which this reality does not wholly coincide. In reference to the perceived reality, reality as "presence-at-hand" is therefore an explanation but, at the same time, also an impoverishment. The scientific activity explicitates an objective aspect of the original perception, but by doing so, it leaves behind real be-ing in the full sense of the term in order to dis-close and explain a certain aspect of that be-ing. On the other hand, this aspect is really an aspect of reality and therefore science remains knowledge of reality. In other words, the explicitation and explanation of the purely objective aspect of reality results in a certain meaning which really belongs to the thing but only from the standpoint of "presence-at-hand." That meaning can be disclosed only through a method and through cognitive processes corresponding to that proper object.[185]

Plurality of Sciences. In a very general way, then, experience is the giving of meaning in an encounter. The term "encounter," however, has here a very broad sense and, as an analogous expression, may serve to indicate widely divergent contacts between man and the world. In theoretical or scientific experience this encounter is always a thematiza-tion in the above-mentioned sense. This thematization can also present itself in very divergent forms. Sciences differ from one another insofar as they differ in thematization. In other words, there are as many sciences as there are ways in which things allow themselves to be encountered in different thematizations.[186] In the non-philosophical sci-ences, as we have indicated, such a change of standpoint always implies the demarcation of a certain thematic field, circumscribed by a certain "horizon of understanding." This demarcation disengages that which is

---

[184] Heidegger, *ibid.,* pp. 8-15 (English ed., pp. 28-35) ; W. Biemel, *Le concept du monde chez Heidegger,* Paris, 1950, p. 8.

[185] de Waelhens, *Une philosophie de l'ambiguïté,* pp. 389-391.

[186] Kwant, *art. cit.* in footnote 175, p. 33.

encountered in natural, unreflected experience in such a way that it becomes an autonomous object.

The root of all those possible objectivations of the sciences is the one world of our original intentionality, the world in which we live. By means of reduction it is in principle always possible to return to this most original field of presence. Our original being-in-and-to-the-world contains an original contact with the world that is always presupposed in every non-original encounter, in every willed dialogue. Now, just as every non-original encounter with the world is an offshoot of our original experience, so also is the proper field of meaning of every science an offshoot and expression of the original and natural world as it manifests itself to us in the original experience. This original and natural world is the world which every concrete and conscious thematization of the sciences intends in all its fullness, but which it dis-closes only in part. The different sciences, which merely aim at this world in which we live, can attain unity in this world insofar as together they hope to explicitate the primordial meaning of this original field of presence in all its fullness.[187]

Philosophy and the World of Original Experience. Unlike the other sciences, philosophy does not speak about a certain kind of be-ings, viewed under a certain aspect, but wants to speak about man himself as encountering the world and about the world as it manifests itself to him in primordial experience. "The first philosophical act, therefore, would be to return to the 'lived' world."[188] Hence the world spoken of by philosophy is not an objective world, projected in abstracting thematization, but the world of our original experience. Its task is to disclose the eidetic structures that are implied in our *original* experience. In attempting this task, philosophy is not concerned with the purely objective aspects of things but with their meaning, which constitutes itself in an original way in our being-to-the-world, i.e., philosophy is interested in reality insofar as it manifests itself to us in that original encounter. "To thematize the structures immersed in the co-existence of perceptive experience, to disengage what we have called their noematic core," says Alphonse de Waelhens, "that is the task belonging to phenomenology."[189] Hence the method to be used is that of intentional

---

[187] Kwant and van den Berk, *art. cit.,* p. 3.
[188] Merleau-Ponty, *op. cit.,* p. 57.
[189] de Waelhens, *op. cit.,* p. 391.

analysis.[190]   However, once the structures provided by our original experience have been phenomenologically analyzed, we must raise questions concerning the modes of being of these structures, and especially the proper modes of being of the be-ings that embody these structures as well as that of man himself who experiences them.   At this point phenomenological reflection becomes ontology.[191]

Since the thematization which forms the basis of philosophy differs essentially from the abstracting and objectifying thematizations performed by the positive sciences, philosophy has to make use of a different method, possess a different mode of intelligibility, a different language, and a different idea of truth and certainty.   Consequently, philosophy and science are radically distinct.

On the other hand, philosophy and science are not in competition with each other, and it is inconceivable that one would make the other superfluous.   As a study of reality, viewed from a certain angle that is based on our original experience, science must always revert to the experience from which it ultimately derived its object.   It is precisely of this experience as such that philosophy speaks.[192]

---

[190] Merleau-Ponty, *op. cit.*, p. 59.
[191] de Waelhens, *op. cit.*, pp. 391-392.
[192] Merleau-Ponty, *Sens et Non-Sens*, pp. 194-195; de Waelhens, *op. cit.*, p. 391; Kwant, *art. cit.* in footnote 175, pp. 38-39.

PART TWO

INTENTIONAL ANALYSIS OF A CON-
TEMPORARY PHYSICAL THEORY:
THE THEORY OF RELATIVITY

Introductory Remarks

Restricted Aim of Parts Two and Three. In the last two parts of this study we will attempt to describe as accurately as possible the proper character of the physicist's activity and of nature as the correlate of the physical standpoint with respect to the world. In this description we will base ourselves on the ideas acquired in the preceding part of this book. For various reasons, however, it appears desirable to restrict this investigation to contemporary physical science.

First, as men of our time, we want most of all to understand our own era; hence we are most interested in acquiring an evaluating judgment regarding physical science as it develops in our time.

Secondly, classical physics constitutes no more than a beginning. Its study of nature remained largely limited to a consideration of the natural phenomena in which a few relatively large bodies move with relatively low velocities. True, in such a relatively simple view of natural events, as that of classical physics, it is easier to discover the essence than in the more complex picture presented by contemporary physics. Yet, on the other hand, it should be evident that it would also be easier to fall for the temptation of speaking of essential characteristics where there is really only question of supposedly essential features.

Finally, by limiting ourselves to contemporary physical science, we can dispense with many involved historical investigations. Of course, wherever the historical character of physical science demands it, we will indicate the bond between classical and contemporary physics, but even then we will limit ourselves to the strictly necessary.

Philosophical Reflection upon Physical Science. As we have seen in Part One, philosophy may be generally characterized as a radical reflection upon being and our knowledge of being. Thus, a philosophical reflection upon contemporary physical science will ultimately have to concentrate on the questions: What, properly speaking, is the physical be-ing? What mode of being must be attributed to nature precisely insofar as it is the intentional correlate of physical science?

The philosopher has to ask these questions in an explicit fashion, but the professional physicist does not remain a complete stranger to them. It is true, of course, that the physicist, *as a physicist,* cannot ask any questions concerning the domain of his scientific research because, with the means which he possesses as a physicist, it is impossible to reply to the question of what the proper character of a physical be-ing is.[1] But this

---

[1] Heidegger, *Was heisst Denken?* pp. 56-58.

does not alter the fact that the physicist, following a natural inclination of his consciousness, often passes from his special science to philosophy and then, in this new attitude toward the world, asks himself, *as a philosopher,* questions concerning the realm of his scientific interest.

Even if we abstract from such explicit reflection on the mode of being proper to the correlate of his physical attitude, the standpoint of the physicist toward the world always contains implicitly a certain view of physical science and of its objective domain. As Husserl says, "An essential idea of nature lies, albeit indefinitely, at its basis. Correlatively, consciousness, functioning as physical experience and at the same time as physical reflection on this experience, possesses its essential phenomenological unity. And this consciousness has its essential correlate in nature. A dominating 'apperception' predetermines what is and what is not an object of physical science, i.e., what is or is not nature in the sense of physical science. This is what has to be clarified."[2]

For the explicitly reflecting philosopher it is of the utmost importance that, before he determines his position, he take cognisance of the physicist's "self-consciousness," wherever it endeavors to arrive at an explicit self-interpretation. Yet of even greater importance would seem to be that he makes an accurate analysis of the above-mentioned implicit "self-consciousness," for that "self-consciousness" is found in all physicists and does not yet contain any philosophical *a priori's.* For this reason we prefer to appeal primarily to this implicit "self-consciousness" in our analysis without, however, disregarding the explicit testimony of physicists.

The following analyses, then, are ultimately concerned with the question of what contemporary physical science manifests about the proper character of the physicist's activity and that of the correlate of his attitude toward the world. In our attempt to solve this question we will make use of the intentional analysis described in the first part of this study. We will utilize, moreover, as much as possible the insights provided by the contemporary logic of the physical sciences and the results attained by the critique of the sciences. We will endeavor to divest our considerations from the influence of philosophical ideas that cannot be reconciled with the conception of philosophy described in Part One.

For purely practical reasons we will have to make a second restriction

---

[2] Husserl, *Ideen,* vol. 2, p. 2.

in this part of our study. Strictly speaking, we would have to make here an intentional analysis of the whole of contemporary physical science. Since such an analysis would exceed the scope of this study, we have decided, after due consideration, to limit ourselves to the theory of relativity. For, as will become apparent, this important theory is sufficiently general to throw light on the proper character of the physicist's activity and on nature as the correlate of the physical attitude toward the world.

CHAPTER FIVE

A FEW HIGHLIGHTS IN THE HISTORY OF THE THEORY OF RELATIVITY

1. *The Philosophers' Distrust of Einstein's Theory*

As early as 1923 Fernand Renoirte wrote that outside the circle of specialists the theory of relativity is often brought into discredit by attaching to the physical terms meanings which they do not have and which the founders of the theory did not at all intend to attribute to them.[3] Since then numerous misunderstandings have been taken away. Quiet prevails now in the camp of the physicists, and this peace is based on solid conviction. Among philosophers, however, there continues to be a great deal of confusion, which even now still arises to a large extent from the fact that a *philosophical* meaning is immediately connected with the terms expressing the *physical* theory.[4] But other factors also play a role; hence it will be useful to say a few words about them here.

Aversion to the Term "Relativity." First of all, the very name of this theory was prejudicial to its reception. For it gave rise to the impression that Einstein had wanted to claim that everything is relative, that the theory "relativizes space and time," and that "by denying simultaneity" it makes many of our established ideas regarding the temporal aspect of things valueless.[5] As Emile Meyerson points out, some followers of the philosophy of Auguste Comte and Ernst Mach tried to make use of the ambiguity suggested by the term "relativity" to propagate the idea that "the relativity of space implies that of our

---

[3] F. Renoirte, "La théorie physique. Introduction à l'étude d'Einstein," *Revue néoscolastique de philosophie,* vol. 25, p. 349.

[4] Cf. N. Hartmann, *Philosophie der Natur. Abriss der speziellen Kategorienlehre,* Berlin, 1950, p. 235. Hartmann himself, however, makes this mistake, e.g., on pp. 245-247. The same must be said of J. Seiler, *Philosophie der unbelebten Natur,* Olten, 1948, pp. 134-166 and G. Bremer, *Wijsgerige aspecten van het natuurkundig tijdbegrip,* Utrecht, 1955.

[5] Cf. A. D. Fokker, *Filosofie in de natuurkunde,* Den Haag, 1949, p. 99.

knowledge in the whole order of ideas and proves, consequently, how useless it would be to try to penetrate into the interior of things."[6] Meyerson goes on to show that Einstein, Eddington, Weyl and many others have protested against that attempt and that the main contention of the theory of relativity is precisely to present the phenomena of nature in a way that they will be the same for any observer.[7]

Nevertheless, the use of the term "relativity" conceals the fact that the theory is really interested in something absolute, viz., the invariant character of the laws of nature, the independence of those laws on the mode of perception.[8]　For this reason efforts have been made to substitute a different name; for instance, one could speak with Adrian Fokker of "chronogeometry."[9]　The reasons for this proposed name will become clear later in this study.

Dependence on Popularizations.　Secondly, the theory of relativity is a clear example of a mathematical, i.e., non-mechanical,[10] theory which is exceedingly difficult to present exactly in its proper and true form without the aid of higher mathematics.[11]　Most non-specialists in theoretical physics—and this includes almost of necessity the overwhelming majority of philosophers—therefore have to rely on scientific popularizations.　Many of these works, however, are valueless from a "scientific" standpoint.　Even the best of them, written by the foremost experts, contain ambiguities and equivocal expressions which do not

---

[6] E. Meyerson, *La déduction relativiste,* Paris, 1925, p. 61.　Cf. also F. Selvaggi, "Il significato della relatività," *Gregorianum,* vol. 33, pp. 418-425. Selvaggi names here, *inter alios,* E. Cassirer (*Zur Einstein'schen Relativitätstheorie,* Berlin, 1923), G. de Ruggiero (*Filosofia del novecento,* Bari, 1934), A. Tilgher (*Relativisti contemporanei,* Roma, 1923), and F. Albergamo (*La critica della scienza del novecento,* Firenze, 1950).　In other words, Selvaggi and Meyerson do not agree about Weyl's conception of this matter.

[7] Meyerson, *op. cit.,* pp. 61-68.　Cf. also H. Rickert, *Die Grenzen der naturwissenschaftlichen Begriffsbildung,* Tübingen, 1921, p. xiv.

[8] Meyerson, *op. cit.,* pp. 78-79; Fokker, "Over de absoluta der chronogeometrie," *Kon. Ned. Acad. der Wetenschappen,* vol. 64, p. 133; "Relativistische studie," *De Gids,* vol. 86, pp. 254-256; Eddington, *Space, Time and Gravitation,* Cambridge, 1953, pp. 30-44; *The Mathematical Theory of Relativity,* Cambridge, 1954, pp. 2-3; W. Mund, "Le langage de la physique," *La relativité de notre connaissance,* by L. de Raeymaeker, W. Mund and J. Ladrière, Louvain, 1948, pp. 71-72.

[9] Fokker, first article quoted in preceding footnote, p. 133.　Elsewhere Fokker speaks of the "theory of invariants" (*Filosofie in de natuurkunde,* p. 89).

[10] Concerning this distinction see Renoirte, *Cosmology,* New York, 1950, pp. 155-169.

[11] Meyerson, *op. cit.,* p. 81.

deceive the specialist but are easily misunderstood by the non-specialist.[12] To this must be added that, although nearly all leading physicists agree about the mathematical core of the theory, they do not exhibit the same unanimity in their popular expressions of this scientific theory. As Eddington observes very correctly, in one of his best works of popularization, "The task is one of interpreting a clear-cut theory, accepted in all its essentials by a large and growing school of physicists—although perhaps not everyone would accept the author's view of its meaning."[13]

Moreover, popularizations often contain striking comparisons, more or less vague admissions, and daring assertions which have little or no basis in the theory itself.[14] The popularizers frequently do not hesitate to present well-intentioned philosophical ideas which, however, are neither the foundation of the mathematical core of the theory nor connected with it. As M. Minnaert points out correctly, such personal hypotheses and philosophical speculations in popular explanations of the theory generally render bad service to the non-specialist for whom those works are written.[15] It is precisely against those comparisons, those daring assertions, and those philosophical presuppositions that the "critical" reviewers direct their attacks. The result is that many are strengthened in their distrust of a theory which appears strange enough as it is.

Extrapolations. Much of the philosophers' critique often arose precisely from such adept extrapolations of certain obscure, inaccurate, and ill-formulated or mis-understood expressions found in popular treatises. Obviously, such a critique is rather easy and, what at first sight is even worse, it often sounds quite convincing. As an example we may quote Einstein's well-known words regarding the concept of simultaneity: "We thus require a definition of simultaneity such that

---

[12] See, e.g., Eddington's statement in *Space, Time and Gravitation*, p. vi: "We abstract from the phenomena that which is peculiar to the position and the motion of the observer; but can we abstract that which is peculiar to the limited imagination of the human brain? We think we can, but only in the symbolism of mathematics. As the language of the poet rings with a truth that eludes the clumsy explanations of his commentators, so the geometry of relativity in its perfect harmony expresses a truth of form and type in nature, which my bowdlerised version misses." See also Meyerson, *op. cit.*, pp. 81-84. Examples of solid popular-scientific works are Einstein, *Relativity. The Special and General Theory*, London, 1954; Einstein and L. Infeld, *The Evolution of Physics*, Cambridge, 1938; Eddington, *Space, Time and Gravitation*, Cambridge, 1953, and *The Nature of the Physical World*, Cambridge, 1948.

[13] Eddington, *Space, Time and Gravitation*, p. v.

[14] Meyerson, *op. cit.*, pp. 79-80.

[15] M. Minnaert, *De sterrenkunde en de mensheid*, Den Haag, 1946, p. 65.

this definition supplies us with a method by means of which, in the present case, [we] can decide by experiment whether or not [two events] occurred simultaneously. As long as this requirement is not satisfied, I allow myself to be deceived as a physicist (and of course the same applies if I am not a physicist), when I imagine that I am able to attach a meaning to the statement of simultaneity."[16]

The critique of this assertion usually begins by equating the non-physicist with the metaphysician, which is more than seems warranted by the text. It then proceeds to argue about "simultaneity" without any qualification instead of about a *physical* concept of simultaneity. Finally, even if Einstein really meant to make the erroneous assertion which that critique tries to attribute to him, it would still leave the theory of relativity wholly untouched because that erroneous element plays no essential role in the theory itself.[17] As we will see later,[18] the core of that theory should be sought in its theses concerning absolute relations and not in the denial of simultaneity.

It happens also that philosophers become acquainted with the theory of relativity through studies pertaining to the so-called philosophy of physical science.[19] In such a case it can easily happen that these philosophers of physical science have a different conception of philosophy than the critics of the theory of relativity. That situation readily leads the critic to transfer his objections against these philosophers to the theory of relativity itself.

Of course, the theory is exceedingly difficult, even if we abstract from its mathematical formulation, because it is concerned with the fundamental notions of positive-scientific thought and those notions are very difficult to formulate in an exact way. In such a situation fictions are sometimes substituted for the truth, especially when one is told that

---

[16] Einstein, *Relativity* . . . , p. 22.

[17] A. van Melsen, *Natuurwetenschap en wijsbegeerte,* Utrecht, 1946, pp. 176-187 (especially pp. 180-184). For the opposite view see W. Pauli, "Relativitätstheorie und Wissenschaft," *Fünfzig Jahre Relativitätstheorie,* Basel, 1956, p. 286, and M. Born, "Physics and Relativity," *ibid.,* p. 259.

[18] See below, pp. 138 and 143. Cf. also Renoirte, "La critique einsteinienne des mesures d'espace et de temps," *Revue néoscolastique de philosophie,* vol. 26, p. 267.

[19] Examples of such works are Meyerson, *La deduction relativiste,* Paris, 1925; H. Weyl, *Philosophy of Mathematics and Natural Science,* Princeton, 1949; H. Margenau, *The Nature of Physical Reality,* New York, 1950; E. Beth, *Natuurphilosophie,* Gorinchem, 1948; Renoirte, *art. cit.* in footnote 18; B. Bavink, *Ergebnisse und Probleme der Naturwissenschaften,* Zürich, 1949; H. Weyl, *Raum, Zeit, Materie,* Berlin, 1923.

prominent physicists had serious objections against the theory or that Einstein, De Sitter, Weyl, Eddington and others never managed to come to full agreement regarding certain points of the theory. The temptation exists then to forget that those points were generally of secondary importance or concerned with the expansion of the theory.[20]

Relativity Versus Classical Physics. Some philosophers who were well versed in classical physics thought at first that the theory of relativity would do away with the whole of classical physics. But classical physics, in spite of all appearances and a real danger of mechanicism, harmonized "marvelously" with the philosophical ideas defended by those philosophers. The theory of relativity, on the other hand, seemed, at least at first, far less amenable. Moreover, with respect to the problem of space and place the theory of relativity went counter to the ether theory, which appeared important to their philosophical interpretation of nature. Thus it is not surprising that all such motives led to a distrust of the theory of relativity.[21]

However, it is not correct that the theory of relativity does away with classical physics. As Fokker writes, "I fail to see that the theory of relativity 'completely upsets all axiomatic and hypothetical foundations of the older study of nature.' It makes those foundations more precise and complements them. It seems to me that the revolutionary force of the theory is generally much overrated. . . . The theory offers an *improved approximation*. It is indeed the theory of the next decimal."[22] In the same sense J. Jeans says: "The two schemes of Einstein and Newton are poles asunder in their physical interpretations, but it would be a mistake to think of the Newtonian scheme as nothing but an accumulation of errors. The quantitative error in Newton's law of gravitation is so small that nearly 200 years elapsed before any error was discovered, or even suspected. . . . And when we come down from the

---

[20] Fokker, "Levensbericht van Albert Einstein. 14 maart 1879-10 april 1955," *Jaarboek der Kon. Ned. Acad. v. Wetenschappen,* 1954-1955. Concerning these points see Fokker, *Relativiteitstheorie,* Groningen, 1929, pp. 275-286; Eddington, *The Mathematical Theory of Relativity,* pp. 149-170, 196-237; P. Jordan, *Schwerkraft und Weltall,* Braunschweig, 1955; Einstein, *The Meaning of Relativity,* London, 1950, Appendix I and App. II, pp. 104-141; M. Born, "Physics and Relativity," *op. cit.* in footnote 17, pp. 244 and 255.

[21] Cf., e.g., G. Heymans, "Lekenvragen ten opzichte van de relativiteitstheorie," *De Gids,* vol. 85, p. 101; P. Hoenen, *Cosmologia,* Rome, 1945, pp. 438-464, 502-511.

[22] Fokker, "Relativistische studie," *De Gids,* vol. 86, pp. 270-271.

heavens to the earth, we find a science of everyday life which is still entirely Newtonian."[23]

Moreover, there is no justification whatsoever for the attempt to maintain an antiquated physical view by means of philosophical arguments. That effort is based on a faulty idea regarding the relationship between philosophy and science. This point will occupy our attention later in this study.[24]

Insufficient Mathematical Knowledge. There are also philosophers who began to study the mathematical theory with enthusiasm, but whose ardor apparently waned after they had absorbed the treatise concerning the Lorentz transformations, with which the theory is introduced in various books. However, the theory itself really begins thereafter. Even thematically speaking, the core of the theory lies not so much in these transformation formulae as in the interpretation which Einstein gave to them in opposition to FitzGerald, Lorentz, and Larmor. If the theory, then, is approached *solely* through these formulae, one will see, at least at first, too much of the negative aspect of the theory, viz., its critique of the classical views concerning space and time. But the positive aspect of the theory is not *immediately* involved in that critique.[25]

All this shows that a considerable amount of confusion has managed to maintain itself among philosophers for the past four decades. Around 1920 the core of the theory and the essence of the philosophical consequences that could be connected with this theory were already more or less known. Yet confusion has continued to exist and for this reason a new reflection on the theory of relativity and its consequences does not seem entirely superfluous.

2. From Classical Mechanics to Relativity

The Crisis of the Classical Theory. Long before Einstein, together with a few other prominent physicists, had laid the foundation for the special theory of relativity, there was something wrong with the mighty edifice of classical physics. With Bernard Bavink, the hidden contradiction may perhaps be described as follows. By virtue of the classical

---

[23] J. Jeans, *The Growth of Physical Science,* Cambridge, 1951, p. 300.
[24] See below, pp. 176-184.
[25] See below, pp. 138-150.

principle of relativity Newtonian mechanics denies that it is possible to determine, either theoretically or experimentally, whether a given closed system is in uniform rectilinear motion. Classical mechanics admits such a possibility only in the case of systems that are subject to acceleration or rotation. Maxwell's electrodynamics, however, together with optics, led to the conclusion that a uniform rectilinear motion of a given system should be determinable in an absolute way. As Bavink expresses it, "The conflict arises through this that Maxwell together with Galileo lead to a result which harmonizes neither with experience in electrodynamics itself nor with the theory and experience of mechanics (Galileo together with Newton)."[26]

Thus, the founders of the theory of relativity were not primarily forced to find a new theory "through certain experimental facts taken *separately,* but through the impossibility of physics to construct a theoretical *frame* in which *all* facts could be placed—in other words, through the difficulty that the worldview of classical physics had become disturbingly blurred."[27] The following brief points may serve to illustrate how disturbing the situation was.[28]

Classical Mechanics and Electric and Optic Phenomena. Classical mechanics assumes that it is possible to discover something about the past of a moving system and to predict something about its future, once we know the present situation and the forces acting on this system. For the planets the active force is Newton's central force of gravitation, the magnitude of which is determined solely by the distance existing between the relevant bodies. The enormous success of this view induced physicists to think that this mechanical idea could be applied consistently to all branches of physics, so that henceforth all natural phenomena were to be explained by the action of attractive or repulsive forces between immutable particles. As a matter of fact, it appeared that the corpuscular structure of matter and the phenomena of heat could be successfully explained on the basis of this view.

In the realm of electric and optical phenomena, however, this mechanical explanation fell short in several respects. A moving charge, for example, exercises influence upon a magnetic needle, but the

---

[26] Bavink, *op. cit.,* pp. 104-105. See also J. Becquerel, *Le principe de la relativité et la théorie de la gravitation,* Paris, 1922, p. 35.

[27] H. Groot, *Geheimen van ruimte en tijd,* Amsterdam, 1947, p. 199.

[28] For what follows cf. Einstein and Infeld, *The Evolution of Physics,* pp. 1-260.

magnitude of the combined forces appeared dependent not only on the distance between charge and needle but also on the velocity of the moving charge. In optics Fresnel's mechanical explanation at first appeared to be more successful, but even there great difficulties soon arose in connection with Maxwell's ether.

Faraday's and Maxwell's investigations led to the introduction of new concepts, the most important of which was that of "field." For, in the realm of electrodynamics it became manifest that the action of currents, magnets, and charges could best be considered in an indirect way by means of so-called "fields," imagined to be somehow connected with the currents. As the theory was further developed, however, those fields, which at first were introduced only as an image, more and more manifested themselves as realities. Moreover, it became evident that a certain energy had to be attributed to those realities. Maxwell was the first physicist who managed to formulate in mathematical equations the quantitative aspect of the laws governing the field theory. "The formulation of these equations is the most important event in Physics since Newton's time, not only because of their wealth of content, but also because they form a pattern for a new type of law. The characteristic features of Maxwell's equations, appearing in all other equations of modern Physics, are summarized in one sentence: Maxwell's equations are laws representing the structure of the field."[29]

As a matter of fact, the mechanical laws which had been formulated since Newton's time were, without exception, concerned with certain particles endowed with mass and charge, while in Maxwell's equations all space plays a role. For, despite the fact that at first the so-called electric and magnetic fields had been conceived as separate realities, it became increasingly clear that, on the basis of the law of conservation of energy, it would be better to speak of a single electromagnetic field capable of explaining satisfactorily the experiments of Faraday and Oersted. According to Maxwell, this electromagnetic field should be conceived as a reality whose action takes place in accordance with his equations and expands through space in a continuous way.

Next, the research of Hertz showed that an oscillating charge causes a so-called "electromagnetic wave." As Maxwell had predicted, it appeared to be a transversal wave, propagating itself in a vacuum with a velocity equal to that of light. The fact that the electromagnetic waves

---

[29] *Ibid.,* pp. 148-149.

and light waves revealed themselves to have the same velocity led to the idea that there would be a very close connection between electromagnetic and optical phenomena. This idea was subsequently developed into a full electrodynamic theory of light by Maxwell.

To see how all this throws light on the starting point of the theory of relativity, it is necessary to make a few additional remarks concerning the classical views of Galileo and Newton.

Galileo's Classical Principle of Relativity. Classical mechanics asserts with Galileo that any body continues in a state of rest or uniform rectilinear motion unless it is prevented by external forces acting upon that body. This law is called Galileo's "law of inertia." At first sight, this law seems so clear that one could wonder what remains to be explained in it. If, however, one takes the case of an observer placed in a rotating chamber, it will be noted that for this observer the law does not work. With respect to his frame of reference the law is not valid. This example teaches us that the interpretation of mechanical events depends on the frame of reference. If, now, we assume—which is not exact—that the laws of classical mechanics are valid for every frame of reference or system of co-ordinates that is firmly connected with the earth, then we can deduce from experiments that the laws of mechanics are valid with respect to all frames of reference which are in a state of uniform rectilinear motion with regard to the first frame of reference. This statement is called the "classical principle of relativity."[30]

If, on the other hand, we have two systems of co-ordinates which are not in uniform rectilinear motion with respect to each other, then the description of the event according to certain "laws of nature" cannot be made in the same way. Science speaks of "inertial systems" with respect to frames of reference for which the law of inertia is valid.[31] We do not yet know whether such inertial systems exist, but we do know that once we have discovered a single such system this discovery implies that there are endless numbers of such systems. For, according to the classical

---

[30] *Ibid.,* p. 165. For a more exact formulation of this principle see Einstein, *The Meaning of Relativity,* pp. 4-22, 23-24; *Relativity . . . ,* pp. 12-15; Selvaggi, "Il significato della relatività," *Gregorianum,* vol. 33, 418-437 (especially pp. 419-420), and "Assoluto e relativo nel tempo," *ibid.,* vol. 28, p. 341. See also below, pp. 121-126.

[31] Einstein and Infeld, *op. cit.,* p. 166; Einstein, *The Meaning of Relativity,* pp. 135-137 (*passim*); Mund, *art. cit.* in footnote 8, pp. 49-50. See also below, pp. 121-126.

principle of relativity, all frames of reference which move in a uniform rectilinear way with respect to that first system will have to be inertial systems also.

As soon as the quantitative aspect of a certain phenomenon has been described with respect to one inertial system, that aspect can be determined also for any other inertial system by means of the so-called "Galileo transformations." On closer inspection of these transformations classical physics appears to start from the assumption that the time corresponding to a certain event is the same for all frames of reference but that the space co-ordinates and the velocity are different for every frame of reference. Although these space co-ordinates and velocities differ for every system of co-ordinates, nevertheless, the change of velocity, the force causing this change, and consequently the natural law in question are invariant with respect to that transformation of co-ordinates.[32]

Difficulties. Galileo's classical principle of relativity applies to all mechanical phenomena. The question, however, is whether it is valid also for *all* phenomena of nature. For a long time it was thought that the reply should be in the affirmative, but later it became evident that such could not be the case. Especially the experiments of Michelson, Morley and others proved conclusive in this matter.[33] Several prominent men of science suspected that fundamental issues were at stake in this problem and tried, each in his own way, to find a solution.[34]

As we will see later, the root of those difficulties dated from Newton's own time. It had managed to remain almost unobserved for two centuries in spite of the fundamental mistake because of the enormous success which classical physics continued to have year after year. On the other hand, there had always been great mathematicians and physicists[35] who felt intuitively that there was a fundamental mistake but were not able to indicate what it was or how it could be eliminated without

---

[32] Einstein, *The Meaning of Relativity,* pp. 24-25; Einstein and Infeld, *op. cit.,* pp. 166-171; Mund, *art. cit.,* pp. 63-64.

[33] Einstein and Infeld, *op. cit.,* p. 177. For this whole matter see *ibid.,* pp. 172-177 and 179-186.

[34] Born, *art. cit.* in footnote 17, pp. 245-248.

[35] Many philosophers likewise protested, with Aristotle and Kant, against Newton's conception of space, but their critique was solely concerned with the objectivity of space. Cf. Selvaggi, "Assoluto e relativo nel tempo," *Gregorianum,* vol. 28, pp. 337-341.

jeopardizing other theories. We may name, for example, Christian Huygens, Leonhard Euler, and Ernst Mach.[36] The hidden contradiction became more apparent only through the interlocking implications of certain experiments which in themselves did not seem to be too closely connected. The most important of these were those of Michelson, Morley, and others.[37] In various ways many great physicists, such as Mach, FitzGerald, Whittaker, Lorentz, Larmor, and Poincaré, went to work on the problem, which still was not clearly formulated. Only in 1905 did Einstein, basing himself on the investigations of those scientists, succeed in laying bare the core of the problem. From a purely mathematical standpoint, Lorentz had already solved it by proposing new transformation formulae to replace the Galileo transformations.[38] Like FitzGerald, however, Lorentz continued to hold fast to Newton's classical ideas of space and time. He considered his transformations as purely auxiliary magnitudes and thus saw himself forced to admit a Lorentz contraction and an Einsteinian time dilatation. With Poincaré, Einstein, however, went much farther[39] and protested against absolute motion and rest as well as absolute space and time.[40]

Einstein's Critique. Classical physics held fast to an absolute time, i.e., a time that is valid in all inertial systems. It conceived time as a physical magnitude which observers, armed with identical clocks, could measure with identical results, even when those observers moved with arbitrary velocities in relation to one another. They also admitted an absolute length, i.e., a length which would be valid in all frames of reference, so that all observers, measuring with identical rods, would find the same measuring numbers for the length of spatial objects, even if they were moving with different velocities in relation to the object to be measured. Within that schema of space and time, they assumed, moreover, that all inertial systems have the same direction.

---

[36] B. Swanenburg, *De verovering der materie,* Utrecht, 1950, pp. 275-276; H. Groot, *Geheimen van ruimte en tijd,* pp. 201-205.

[37] Eddington, *Space, Time and Gravitation,* pp. 203-213; Swanenburg, *op. cit.,* pp. 275-278; W. Dampier, *A History of Science and Its Relation with Philosophy and Religion,* Cambridge, 1948, pp. 399-402.

[38] For Lorentz' transformation formulae and their significance, see Fokker, *Relativiteitstheorie,* pp. 1-50; J. Synge, *Relativity: the Special Theory,* Amsterdam, 1956, pp. 69-112; Einstein, *The Meaning of Relativity,* pp. 27-53; Bavink, *Ergebnisse und Probleme* . . . , pp. 105-107; Mund, *art. cit.* in footnote 8, pp. 65-71.

[39] Bavink, *op. cit.,* pp. 107-111; Born, *art. cit.* in footnote 17, pp. 244-249.

[40] Cf. Groot, *op. cit.,* pp. 201-203.

Einstein criticized Newton's ideas of space and time in this sense that, to begin with, he denied that the concept of "simultaneity at a distance" can ever be an immediate datum of our perception. This simultaneity can be made measurable only through a new definition. By postulating, alongside the special principle of relativity, that the velocity of light in a vacuum is constant in all directions, that new definition of simultaneity-at-a-distance leads to the relativation of simultaneity: two events that are simultaneous within a given frame of reference need not be considered to be simultaneous also within other frames of reference. Through Lorentz' transformation Einstein arrived at a similar relativation of the measurement of length. At the same time it became clear that the phenomena which Lorentz had tried to explain through a theory of contraction and dilatation and his theory of electrons now appeared to be merely the result of different ways of perceiving and comparing. Einstein's principle also offered a ready and plausible explanation for the experiments of Michelson and others.[41]

This fundamental vision of space and time was in harmony on nearly all points with the known physical laws of nature, with kinematics, mechanics, electrodynamics, optics, atomic physics, nuclear physics, astrophysics, and cosmology. True, there were numerous slight differences between the findings of classical physics and relativistic physics. But in practically all points which could be verified experimentally the decision was without any reasonable doubt in favor of the new physics.[42]

For the mathematical development of the theory Eugene Minkowski, a senior contemporary of Einstein, became very important. He was able to supply Einstein with the means to do away with the old separation of space and time as autonomous entities and to give a much more convenient and more objective representation of spatio-temporal events in a four-dimensional continuum. Minkowski's ideas contain implicitly the doctrine of absolute intervals according to space and time between real events. In his later years Einstein gave this doctrine an increasingly

---

[41] Cf. Einstein, *The Meaning of Relativity*, pp. 25-28; Einstein and Infeld, *The Evolution of Physics*, pp. 186-209; Eddington, *Space, Time and Gravitation*, pp. 30-44; *The Nature of the Physical World*, pp. 1-35; Born, *art. cit.*, pp. 249-250.

[42] Fokker, *Relativiteitstheorie*, pp. 184-196 and 240-253; Eddington, *The Mathematical Theory of Relativity*, pp. 85-93 and *passim; Space, Time and Gravitation*, pp. 110-135; Bavink, *op. cit.*, pp. 119-126; Dampier, *op. cit.*, pp. 408-409. For a more recent confirmation of the theory, see *Sky and Telescope*, vol. 8 (1954), p. 339; and for the eclipse of June 20, 1955 on Ceylon see *Hemel en Dampkring*, vol. 54 (1956), pp. 149-151.

more central place in his theory, to such an extent that at present there are treatises which begin the study of the special and the general theory of relativity with this doctrine. The effect of this procedure is that the theory of relativity gains in clarity and that it is possible to emphasize the positive aspect of the theory much more than can be done in a primarily historical explanation of it.[43]

These few remarks touch the relevant problems only very superficially. We do not think it necessary to delve more deeply into them here because there is an abundance of scientific and more popular books about the theory. Moreover, in the remaining chapters of this study we will have to revert to the most essential aspects of the theory in order to make it possible to compare the theory of absolute relations with the philosophy of inorganic nature.

The theory of relativity is a very broad theory because it makes important contributions to nearly every issue of physics and is able to coordinate several large areas of classical physics.[44] We will limit ourselves here to the core of the theory, viz., the doctrine of absolute relations according to space and time. That this doctrine really is the core of the theory of relativity can be clarified only later. At present, we merely wish to point out that this assertion is supported by such prominent physicists and philosophers as Eddington,[45] Fokker,[46] Synge,[47] Jeans,[48] Robb,[49] Jordan,[50] Renoirte,[51] and Einstein himself.[52]

---

[43] Cf., e.g., Einstein, *The Meaning of Relativity;* Eddington, *The Mathematical Theory of Relativity;* J. Synge, *Relativity* . . . ; Fokker, *Relativiteitstheorie.* For the whole matter see Einstein, *op. cit.,* pp. 29-31; Einstein and Infeld, *op. cit.,* pp. 209-219.

[44] For the importance of the theory of relativity with reference to the major realms of physical science see, alongside the above-mentioned works of Einstein, Eddington, Fokker, Synge, and Jordan, also G. Sizoo, *Kernphysica,* Den Haag, n.d., pp. 30-32; Swanenburg, *op. cit.,* pp. 278-280.

[45] Eddington, *The Mathematical Theory* . . . , pp. 8-16.

[46] Synge, *Relativity* . . . , p. 19.

[47] Fokker, "Over de absoluta . . . ," (see footnote 8), *passim;* "Wiskunde en natuurkunde," *Nederlands tijdschrift voor Natuurkunde,* vol. 9 (1943), pp. 223-224; *Filosofie in de natuurkunde,* p. 99.

[48] Jeans, *op. cit.,* pp. 293-301.

[49] A. Robb, *Geometry of Space and Time,* Cambridge, 1936.

[50] P. Jordan, *Schwerkraft und Weltall,* pp. 55-62 and *passim.*

[51] Renoirte, *art. cit.* in footnote 3, p. 375 and in footnote 19, pp. 276, 297-298.

[52] Einstein, *The Meaning of Relativity,* p. 35; see also P. Bridgman, *The Logic of Modern Physics,* New York, 1927, p. 73.

CHAPTER SIX

PHYSICAL MAGNITUDES—
MEASUREMENT

1. The Aim of the Theory of Relativity

The theory of relativity is a very broad theory, consisting of several, clearly distinct but nonetheless intimately connected parts. Its starting point lies in a very refined critique of a few fundamental postulates of classical physics. This critique became necessary when certain experiments went against the ideas of the classical synthesis. In its critique the theory proceeds from the idea that the only experimental datum acceptable as a starting point of physics must be a number supplied by measuring instruments. A logical consequence of this position is that all physical magnitudes can be defined only by means of the operational method.

Classical physics, however, accepted ideas concerning space and time, distance and duration, systems of co-ordinates, etc. which were based on rather arbitrary *a priori* assumptions, often derived from philosophy, and which could not at all be considered to be definitions in the sense demanded by the operational method. The founders of the theory of relativity were of the opinion that precisely these arbitrary *a priori* assumptions caused the difficulties encountered in the above-mentioned experiments. In other words, they observed that classical physics was not entirely objective. True, the influence of the observing subject had been eliminated almost scrupulously from the observation of physical magnitudes. However, in doing so, a mistake had been made: all observations had been uncritically and unreservedly referred to a certain "ideal" observer, without keeping in mind that the results discovered in this way would *therefore* have value *only* for this observer.

The question which the theory of relativity asks in this matter is: Is it not possible to arrive at a description of the world in which the laws of nature can be formulated independently of any observer whatsoever? The theory does not want to accept any statement of physics as a really

111

objective law unless it can be verified by *any* observer. For objective laws, absolute relations interconnecting the events of the world, have, by definition, to be independent of the observer. They have to be invariant with respect to any change of standpoint, since they express relations between things and do not want to indicate at the same time the standpoint from which these relations are seized by observers. Hence, for the theory of relativity all systems of co-ordinates have to be in principle equivalent when there is question of formulating laws of nature (the general theory of relativity). Methodologically speaking, this principle becomes the criterion for the exactness of physical assertions.

With the aid of the changed ideas concerning physical space and time implicitly contained in the above-mentioned principle, the theory then proceeds to develop its own views. In this development the absolutely elementary invariant relation that precedes any particular measurement of space or time takes the place of the classical absolutes and thus becomes the foundation of the invariable character proper to the laws of nature.[53]

2. *The Measurement of Physical Magnitudes*

We may begin this part of our study with a consideration of a few technical terms. Although by doing so we anticipate somewhat on subsequent developments, it will be useful to explain them here, so that later we do not have to interrupt our train of thought.

Physical System, State, and Physical Magnitudes. By a "physical system" we mean the physical entity conceived to be the bearer or substratum of a certain complex of physical properties. In this sense we may call a material particle, a wave, or an electromagnetic field a physical system. In a broader sense the term can be applied also to a stone or a tree, for example.

Every system possesses a complex of observable properties. Most of these properties can change in time. The complex of the mutable properties of a certain system at a given moment is called the "state" of that system at that particular moment. The observable properties, however, of a system are meaningful for the physicist only insofar as they are measurable and therefore can be expressed in metric numbers.

---

[53] Cf. Renoirte, *art. cit.* in footnote 19, pp. 274-276; Bavink, *op. cit.*, pp. 105-111; Eddington, *Space, Time and Gravitation*, pp. *v*, 30-44, 180-186; Einstein *The Meaning of Relativity*, pp. 28-30, 54-55.

The term "physical magnitudes" is used to indicate the observable properties of a system, taken precisely insofar as it is determined by metric numbers.[54]

Definition of Physical Magnitudes. The problem is how these physical magnitudes have to be defined, since non-ambiguity, clarity and exactness are absolute requirements of positive science. Restricting ourselves to the modern standpoint, we must say that several views are taken of this problem. The pedagogists among the physicists demand that every physical quantity have only one definition, even though it is true that they permit several derivative secondary definitions when there is any need for them. Rudolf Carnap and Paul Bridgman, however, do not agree with them, but are satisfied with demanding that the different definitions be of the same type. There are considerable differences between these two in the further development of their view.[55]

Carnap. For Carnap, the evolution of a physical definition goes through three stages.[56] In the first stage, which is more qualitative, one endeavors to circumscribe prescientific concepts more accurately by means of the inductive method. In the second stage, which is quantitative, one arrives at the above-mentioned physical magnitudes, which derive their entire meaning from the way they are measured. Their whole meaning consists of the conditions under which certain metric numbers are ascribed to a given system, viewed in a certain respect. Hence for Carnap, to define a physical quantity is to formulate rules according to which certain numbers should be attributed to a given system in a certain respect. The last stage, which is abstract, leads to the construction of a four-dimensional continuum in which one can represent the physical event in the form of a four-dimensional scheme. This idea was developed by Minkowski in connection with the theory of relativity; but, says Carnap, it is "in itself independent of that theory and can be used for the expression of any theory concerning the physical event." The second stage especially has been developed by Carnap with great clarity and in a strictly logical way.[57]

Bridgman's Operational Method. Bridgman, on the other hand, does not follow Carnap in his approach to the problem from the standpoint of logic, but starts with a critical reflection on the methods actually used in

---

[54] H. Margenau, *The Nature of Physical Reality,* New York, 1950, pp. 171-177.
[55] Margenau, *op. cit.,* pp. 220-223.
[56] R. Carnap, *Physikalische Begriffsbildung,* Karlsruhe, 1926.
[57] Carnap, *op. cit.,* p. 56; Margenau, *op. cit.,* pp. 226-231.

physics.[58] In this way he came to the conclusion that the so-called "operational method" is the most fruitful. He also makes measurement the core of every physical definition, but he puts the accent on the observer rather than the thing. According to Carnap, measurable properties are determined by the way in which nature reacts to the changing conditions, but according to Bridgman, the observer determines the properties through his operations. At first, Bridgman conceived these operations as experimental handling through instruments, but later he tried to give an entirely different meaning to them. Most physicists, however, follow him only in the original sense he attached to the term. It seems to us that there is no essential difference between Bridgman's method, conceived in this sense, and the second stage of Carnap's method.[59]

Subsequently, Henry Margenau was able to show that, in addition to the definition by the operational method, physical science should use another type of definition, which he called "constitutive definition." This type of definition does not flow from the operations performed on the objects of nature, but arise from physical laws and theories. For instance, a temporal duration is operationally defined by reference to a clock, but the constitutive definition will say that time is the independent variables in the equations of mechanics.[60]

As early as 1905 Einstein, in developing the special theory of relativity, had followed the method which Bridgman was later to call the "operational method."[61] In 1920 he again appealed to this method in connection with the general theory of relativity.[62] Since Einstein, followed by most modern physicists, defines physical magnitudes by means of the operational method and since the core of this method consists of measuring the observable properties of physical systems, it appears important to reflect once more on the meaning of the concept "measurement."

Measurement. Even in everyday life, but much more so in the positive sciences, man tries to complement a qualitative description of

---

[58] Bridgman, *op. cit.; The Nature of Some of Our Physical Concepts,* New York, 1952.

[59] Margenau, *op. cit.,* pp. 231-232.

[60] Margenau, *op. cit.,* pp. 232-236. Cf., however, H. Weyl, *Philosophy of Mathematics and Natural Science,* pp. 139-151.

[61] Bridgman, *The Logic of Modern Physics,* pp. 1-2, 3-9.

[62] Einstein, *Relativity . . . ;* cf. also Synge, *Relativity . . . ,* p. 7; Eddington, *The Mathematical Theory . . . ,* pp. 1-7, 136.

nature with a quantitative description. He has two means at his disposal, viz., counting and measuring. Counting can be used only when there is question of a collection consisting of distinct, individual things or events. Hence the result of counting is always a whole number. All counting ultimately amounts to the counting of events experienced one after the other. If things or events are simultaneous, they are counted by being pointed to one after the other. Measuring can be done only when there is question of a physical object that is continuous or at least considered to be continuous. Physics knows several kinds of measurements, but in principle all of them can be reduced to the measurement of length. And ultimately all measurement by means of measuring length is reduced to counting.[63]

Measuring implies at least three distinct elements: an object, or rather a *physical system,* on which a certain operation will be performed; a observable *property* of this system whose "value" will be determined by this operation; and an *instrument* by means of which the operation will be made. Because several measuring instruments are available for the measurement of any observable property, this property, as a physical quantity, cannot be identified with the measuring operation itself. Nonetheless, the two are intimately connected because the operation in question will have to result in the definition of the observable property.

Accordingly, physical systems, observable properties, and instruments are essential requirements of any measurement. Yet, of themselves, they are not sufficient. One can speak of a measurement only when the operation connecting these three elements results in a metric number. If no such number results, there is at most question of an experiment or of an observation. On the other hand, it is not necessary that the resulting number be entirely exact, for even an inexact measurement remains a measurement. Physical science does not normally accept the result of a single measuring operation as exact but demands as a rule that a whole series of measurements be made and submitted to the statistical method.[64] Quantum mechanics has raised entirely new problems with respect to the question of measurement, but they need not concern us here.[65]

From the fact that physics bases its definitions on measurements with

---

[63] Carnap, *op. cit.,* pp. 14-16.

[64] Margenau, *op. cit.,* pp. 369-375; For a different formulation see Carnap, *op. cit.,* pp. 16-22.

[65] Margenau, *op. cit.,* pp. 356-388.

the aid of the operational method, some have drawn the conclusion that the physicist is interested *solely* in measurable relationships. It is hardly necessary to point out that such a conclusion goes too far.[66]

3. *Demands to be Met by the Definition of a Physical Quantity*

If we place ourselves on the standpoint in which Carnap and Bridgman, abstracting from the method, are in agreement,[67] then we must say that "the definition of a physical magnitude consists of the establishment of the rules according to which a quantitative value is to be ascribed to the objects."[68] In other words, the meaning of the physical quantity consists in this that metric numbers can be attributed to certain physical objects; and as long as it is not exactly determined how this attribution is to be made, the magnitude in question is not defined, so that any further information about it is meaningless.[69]

Topological and Metric Rules of Definition. To define a physical magnitude fully, two topological and three metric rules have to be established and followed. Concerning these rules the following points are to be noted.

In the topological definition of a physical quantity it should be kept in mind that a certain kind of magnitude is introduced on the basis of the experience that between certain objects of a particular physical realm there exist two relations, namely, one transitive symmetric relation and one transitive asymmetric relation. The first of these leads us to a certain conception of the idea "equality"; the second leads us to the concept of the particular quantity, which usually is conceived as a one-dimensional scalar magnitude. On the basis of this consideration the rule is that the ascription of metric numbers to the physical systems of this particular realm has to be made in such a way that:

1. equal numbers are ascribed to those objects between which the above-mentioned transitive symmetric relation exists;

2. a greater or smaller number is to be ascribed to a physical system which has a transitive asymmetric relation to another system of the same realm than to this other system.

---

66 Margenau, *op. cit.*, p. 174.
67 Margenau, *op. cit.*, p. 231.
68 Carnap, *op. cit.*, pp. 20-21.
69 Carnap, *op. cit.*, p. 21.

The quantity, however, has to be determined not only topologically, i.e., it is not sufficient to indicate when two quantities will be equal or what their "sequence" is in case they are unequal. Hence it is necessary also to make a metric definition, which tries to establish its determined numeric value in three stages. First, the division of the scale has to be established, i.e., we have to come to an agreement about the question when we will say that two distances of the scale division, two differences of magnitude, will be called equal. Aside from this essential point, two others have to be established. A decision has to be made regarding the choice of the zero point on the agreed scale. In other words, we must make an agreement concerning the question of when the value of zero will be ascribed to a particular system with respect to a certain magnitude. Finally, a decision has to be made regarding the choice of a unit of measurement.[70]

4. The Classical Idea Concerning the Measurements of Length and Time

For our purpose here the measurement of lengths and temporal duration is especially important. Hence it will be useful briefly to illustrate the preceding general consideration with examples referring to those two processes of measurement. Although Carnap's work was written nearly twenty-five years after the origin of the theory of relativity, his study of the classical view may be followed here, we believe, because he explicitly wants to abstract from the disputed points.[71]

Measurement of Length. The measurement of length is the most fundamental measurement made in physics, and all other processes of measurement can in principle be reduced to it. The fact of experience on which all measurement of length is based is the existence of so-called rigid bodies. These bodies have a very useful property, viz., once their edges are congruent, they continue to remain congruent. The congruence of these edges is a transitive symmetric relation, i.e., if it exists between a and b as well as between b and $c,$ then it exists also between a and $c.$

It often happens that two edges of such bodies are not fully congruent and that, for instance, a covers b only in part. This relation also is permanent and transitive, but it is not symmetric. In other words, if it

---

[70] Carnap, *op. cit.,* pp. 21-23.
[71] Carnap, *op. cit.,* pp. 37-38.

exists between *a* and *b* as well as between *b* and *c,* then it exists also between *a* and *c,* but if it exists between *a* and *b,* it does not exist, of course, between *b* and *a.*

Applying all this to the above-mentioned rules for the measurement of physical magnitudes, we must say, first of all, that two edges of two rigid bodies are called equal and given the same metric number if, and only if, they are congruent with each other. Hence if two edges cover each other only in part, in such a way that *a* covers only a part of *b,* then a smaller number has to be ascribed to *a* than to *b.*

In principle there is no limit to our freedom in determining the division of the scale. In practice, however, preference is given, of course, to the division which will give the most simple form to the laws of nature. For this reason, in the measurement of length the division of the scale is made in such a way that the length of the distance between two immediately succeeding measuring lines is equal to that of two other similar lines of the measuring rod. This agreement is so natural and so universally accepted that one could hardly discover any other reasonable possibility.

The zero point on the scale division may be arbitrarily determined in this case. We ascribe the length "zero" to the distance between two points when these points spatially coincide. Regarding the choice of the unit to be used for the measurement of length, there are no reasons based on the nature of the magnitude to be measured. In practice the unit of measurement is the meter.[72]

Measurement of Time. With respect to the measurement of time, if we limit ourselves to events that happen in close proximity, one can say that those events are simultaneous which are perceived at the same time. This description does not contain a circular definition because physical science may presuppose as known our psychical awareness of time.

If, with respect to events occurring in close proximity, one event is perceived before another, a smaller number should be assigned to the former, because being-earlier-perceived is a transitive asymmetric relationship and, on the basis of psychical experiences, we assume that the temporal order assigned to events should be one-dimensional.

After defining the topological structure of time in this way, one can proceed to determine the measurement of time. The definition of the scale division demands here that we indicate when two temporal

---

[72] Carnap. *op. cit.,* pp. 24-33.

durations will be said to be equal. To do so, we must make use of a periodic event which either is easily observable or can be easily built into some kind of apparatus. The term "periodic" does not indicate whether or not all the periods in question are "of the same length." All we can do is *define* being-of-the-same-length with the aid of those periods. In practice, several procedures can be followed. One can choose, for example, man's pulse beat, the rotation of a wheel, a pendulum clock, or the orbit of the earth or the moon.

The measurement of time has no natural starting point; hence the zero point on the scale has to be determined arbitrarily. The unit chosen for the measurement of time is a certain constantly repeated, observable event which has given us years, days, hours, and seconds.[73]

---

[73] Carnap, *op. cit.*, pp. 37-41.

CHAPTER SEVEN

EINSTEIN'S CRITIQUE ON THE CLASSICAL IDEAS OF MEASURING SPACE AND TIME

1. The Problems: Isochronism and Synchronism

What has been said above about the measurement of space and time applies up to a point to both classical physics and the theory of relativity, for, with Carnap, we have tried to abstract as much as possible from disputed points.[74] If, however, we want to appreciate Einstein's critique on the classical ideas of space and time at its true value, we must first place ourselves on the standpoint of classical physics with respect to the disputed points. We then meet the following two problems:

1. What is the standpoint of classical physics with respect to the measurement of lengths, especially when the bodies to be measured cannot be immediately brought into contact with a measuring rod?

2. What is the classical view regarding the measurement of temporal durations, especially when there is question of events that happen at great distances from one another?

For practical reasons we will begin with the last-named problem.[75]

As we have said above, by measurement in general we mean to ascribe, according to pre-established fixed rules, certain measuring numbers to a particular, observable property of a physical system by means of one or more instruments.[76] With respect to the measuring of time, only two major problems present themselves. The first of these is concerned with the structure of the scale division to be chosen. It will have to be solved by trying to find a uniform motion which in one way or another can be

---

[74] Cf. pp. 133-135.

[75] We will omit the first point because classical physics did not see any fundamental difficulties in the measurement of the length of moving bodies. However, see pp. 130-135 of this book.

[76] See above, pp. 117-119. Cf. also Margenau, *op. cit.,* pp. 369-375, and Carnap, *op. cit.,* pp. 14-21.

divided into continuous, successive, and equal parts. This question is usually called the problem of the ideal clock or of isochronism. It pertains to the metric definition of the physical quantity "time." The second problem is concerned with the question of how certain "readings" of this one ideal clock coincide with the beginning and the end of the events to be measured if this clock itself is not present in these points. This is called the problem of observing simultaneity or synchronism. It pertains to the topological definition of the physical magnitude "time."

2. Isochronism According to Classical Physics

The Classical Definition of Isochronism. To find a *physical* solution of the problem of isochronism, classical physics early began to look for a uniform periodic motion. The difficulty involved in this search was, of course, that the solution of the problem has to be known before one can determine that a motion is uniform. The only thing to do, if a circular definition was to be avoided, was to define equal durations of time somewhat arbitrarily. In other words, that definition resembled to some extent the definitions used in mathematics, even though this resemblance was not always clearly realized.[77] The only way of understanding the meaning and value of such a definition is to investigate how classical physics arrived at its definition.

According to Poincaré, the notion of time is fairly simple as long as one remains within the domain of man's conscious life. It is easy to distinguish actually present experiences from remembrances of past sensations and expectations of future sensations. Man also knows very well what it means for one event to be experienced before the other. And if he says that two data of consciousness are simultaneous, he wants to express that they wholly compenetrate each other, so that an analysis cannot separate them without doing violence to them. Finally, the order in which we arrange our conscious phenomena is not arbitrary, but imposes itself as irreversible. However, within the domain of consciousness we have no immediate experience of the equality of two time intervals. If we say that the time interval between twelve and one o'clock is just as long as that between two and three o'clock, our statement may have a certain meaning from the psychical standpoint, but the expression "just as long" has no *physical* content. A physicist can

---

[77] Eddington, *The Mathematical Theory* . . . , pp. 1-7. Cf. also *ibid.*, p. 136.

admit that expression only if he exactly defines what is meant by "just as long." Let us see, then, how that definition was obtained.[78]

For the past few centuries man has used pendulum clocks to measure time. It was implicitly established by definition that the ticks of this clock indicated equal lengths. Later it became apparent that this idea was only a provisional approximation, for changes of temperatures, variations in air pressure, transfer to a different latitude, and other factors cause constant slight changes in the running of such a clock. True, one can try to eliminate such factors as much as possible, but even then one will never obtain more than an approximative value, for electric, magnetic, and other factors continue to cause disturbances. In fact, even the best clocks had to be corrected from time to time. These corrections were made on the basis of astronomical observations. In making that kind of correction, it was assumed that the "stellar clock" always indicates periods of equal length, i.e., that equally long periods are required for the repeated passages of a given star through its meridian. Thus the stellar day, the duration of the earth's rotation, was taken to be the constant unit for the measurement of time. "By a new definition it was admitted that two complete rotations of the earth around its axis have the same duration."[79]

The astronomers, however, were not satisfied with this new definition. Many of them thought that the tides were bound to exercise a braking influence on the velocity of the earth's rotation, so that this velocity would constantly become smaller. This idea gave, at the same time, a reasonable explanation for the apparent acceleration of the moon's motions, which was contrary to the relevant laws governing these motions in accordance with Newton's principles.

Inaccuracies and Poincaré's Solution. One could say, of course, that all this is of little importance and that such problems are best explained by keeping in mind that our measuring instruments are inevitably imperfect. In other words, it is enough to imagine a perfect or ideal clock. Although we can never make such a clock, nevertheless, that clock is sufficient to endow our definition of simultaneity with a sharp and exact meaning. "Unfortunately, that exactness is not there." For a postulate is implied when we make use of a clock to measure time, and this postulate is that the durations of identical phenomena are equal.

---

[78] H. Poincaré, *La valeur de la science,* Paris, 1912, pp. 35-38. Cf. also Einstein, *The Meaning of Relativity,* pp. 1-2.

[79] Poincaré, *op. cit.,* p. 39.

Differently expressed, the same causes always need the same length of time to produce the same effects. At first, this statement seemed to be a good definition of the equality of two temporal durations. On closer inspection, however, it becomes evident that this definition also is not tenable. For in physical reality a cause does not act in complete isolation, but there is always a complex of causes at work, and the role each of them plays in producing the effect can never be fully isolated. If a physicist nonetheless insists on isolating such a cause, the result of his investigation can never have more than an approximative value. Accordingly, all that remains of the old definition of equal lengths of time is this: causes which are *more or less* equal need *more or less* the same time to produce *more or less* the same effects.

To solve the impasse, Poincaré appealed to extrinsic arguments. By way of the principle of conservation of energy and Newton's law of gravitation, he finally arrived at this definition for the equality of two time intervals: "Time must be defined in such a way that Newton's law and that of the *vis viva* [i.e. kinetic energy] are verified."[80]

However, Newton's law is based only on observations; hence as such it cannot have more than an approximative value.[81] As a consequence, we still have only an approximative definition for the equality of time intervals. If, on the other hand, we define this equality in a different way, the experiments on which Newton's law of gravitation was based at the time will lose the meaning they possessed then. The result of this would be that this Newtonian law would have to be modified and that it would become much more complex. Thus, Poincaré was finally induced to define the equality of two time intervals in this way: "Time must be defined in such a way that the equations of mechanics are as simple as possible." This definition implies that one measurement of time is not more valuable than another. In fact, the measurement which physical science accepts is the one which, *physically* speaking, appears to be most suitable.[82]

Physically Exact Sense by Definition. Before the critique of Poincaré and Einstein, many thought that they knew exactly what was meant by two equal time intervals. So far as they were concerned, the whole question amounted in practice to this that by means of suitable instruments one verified the equality of the intervals. But, evidently,

---

[80] Poincaré, *op. cit.,* pp. 39-44.
[81] Poincaré, *op. cit.,* pp. 248-261.
[82] Poincaré, *op. cit.,* pp. 44-45.

the terms used by physics cannot have an exact sense if one cannot describe the process by which the point at issue can be exactly observed. The expression "equal lengths of time" itself, therefore, has a physically exact sense only if one, be it through a more or less arbitrary decision, can describe a material process which results *by definition* in these equal time intervals.

A Privileged System of Reference. Even more than that is involved. For, if we want to verify the natural laws governing celestial mechanics by means of experimentally discovered measures, we have not only to measure time intervals according to the assumed definition, but also to localize the position of the fixed stars in a certain frame of description. The choice of this frame of description was likewise not restricted by the necessity to select one particular system, although the laws of celestial mechanics did not appear to hold for any arbitrary system of reference. For this reason the systems for which these laws do hold were called "privileged systems of reference." Among those privileged systems there is one that occupies a special position. This privileged system, which is named after Galileo, is that system which has its center in the center of our solar system and whose axes have a special direction with respect to the whole of fixed stars. Hence in reference to this system the fixed stars have no rotational velocity, the center of our solar system is in "absolute" rest, and the planets describe orbits determined by Newton's law of gravitation. Moreover, all systems of reference which are at rest in relation to this system share in its privileges with respect to the laws of nature. Thus, we may say that Galileo's fundamental frame of description consists of a complex of equivalent Cartesian systems of co-ordinates, viz., the inertial systems.

The Classical Principle of Relativity. It appeared, moreover, that any frame of description which with respect to Galileo's fundamental system moves in a rectilinear uniform motion may be called a privileged Galileo system. For this reason classical physics formulated in its principle of relativity the following assertion: "If, relative to K, K^1 is a uniformly moving co-ordinate system devoid of rotation, then natural phenomena run their course with respect to K^1, according to exactly the same general laws as with respect to K."[83] The same principle can be formulated also in this way: phenomena of mechanics are determined by exactly the same laws in either of these frames of description, *provided*

---

[83] Einstein, *Relativity* . . . , p. 13. Cf. also Eddington, *Space, Time and Gravitation*, p. 20.

these two frames are moving with a rectilinear, uniform motion, devoid of rotation, with respect to each other. Or also: the formulation of the laws of nature is independent of the fact that the systems of co-ordinates in which these laws are described are, in respect of one another, in a state of uniform rectilinear motion.

From the standpoint of mechanics, then, we have no right to assert that one of these systems is "absolutely" at rest and that the others are in "absolute" motion with respect to this system. The terms "absolute rest" and "absolute motion" have no meaning in mechanics that can be formulated in an exact sense because we have no means by which we can select, at least within mechanics, one privileged system rather than the other. An appeal to an absolute space which cannot be measured is useless in this matter.[84]

All this implies that the concept of isochronism, as defined in classical physics, strictly speaking, lacks all *absolute* meaning from the *physical* standpoint. Thus, it is not surprising that, as we will see, the theory of relativity attacked classical physics in this point.

3. The Standpoint of Classical Physics with Respect to Synchronism

The Problem of Synchronism. If we consider the problem of synchronism, we notice at once that a *psychical* definition of simultaneity is useless here.[85] Aside from the fact that such a definition would never lead to exact results, the introduction of such a definition into that problem is objectionable because without sufficient reasons it transfers psychical time from consciousness to everything outside us that is now perceived by us. Finally, the spontaneous notion of simultaneity admits "a kind of 'super consciousness' which sees everything and classifies every-thing *in its time,* just as we classify, *in our time,* the little we see."[86] In other words, the spontaneous view believes, but without ground, in the existence of a "world-time and a world-wide now."[87]

In the preceding pages we have pointed out that, strictly speaking, one needs to have already a definition of isochronism in order to arrive at

---

[84] Einstein, *ibid.,* pp. 9-15; *The Meaning of Relativity,* pp. 23-31.

[85] Poincaré, *op. cit.,* p. 48.

[86] Poincaré, *op. cit.,* p. 47.

[87] Cf. Eddington, *The Mathematical Theory . . . ,* pp. 8, 23-25; *The Nature of the Physical World,* pp. 36-41; Bridgman, *The Logic of Modern Physics,* pp. 74-77.

such a definition and that a circular definition can be avoided only by having recourse to an artificial definition. A similar remark applies to synchronism. To define it, one should know exactly what is meant by "in that place where I am not and at the moment that I here and now look at my clock, this event takes place." In other words, one has to have at his disposal a definition of simultaneity at a distance, which is precisely the problem of synchronism.

The Classical Definition of Simultaneity. Classical physics tried to overcome this difficulty by defining the concept of simultaneity in such a way that in this case also the laws of nature could be formulated in the simplest possible way. Its definition was based on two postulates, viz., that light has a constant velocity and that this velocity is the same in all directions.[88]

The naive view considered simultaneous whatever reaches our eyes in a single glance. But great problems arose when it was discovered that light also has a finite velocity. The first question which has to be solved here may perhaps be described in the following way: How is an experiment to be described through which, at least theoretically, one can verify at any moment and at any place what is meant by the statement that two clocks, one of which is here-now and the other at a distance from the first, constantly indicate the same hour?

There are three ways in which physicists have tried to define simultaneity. The first appealed to an absolutely fixed body; the second was based on the postulate of absolute motions; and the third tried to restrict itself to the known facts.

The first proposed solution conceives the simultaneity of distant events in exactly the same way as when there is question of events happening in close proximity. The difficulty, however, is that two distant events can be called simultaneous in the *physical* sense of the term only if light has an infinite velocity. When that velocity was found to be finite, they had recourse to some kind of fixed body situated between the two events and capable of transmitting instantaneous signals.

The second solution denied the existence of such a body and consequently of signals having an infinite velocity. Postulating the existence of absolute space and time, Newton was able to give an exact meaning to the concept "absolute velocity." At the same time the concepts of isochronism and synchronism acquired thereby an exact

---

[88] Poincaré, *op. cit.*, pp. 57-58, 54-55.

meaning. For it was now possible to say that two time intervals are equal *by definition* if during these intervals light traverses equal distances in absolute space. And to observe the absolute simultaneity of two events separated by a distance, it is sufficient to occupy an absolutely immobile point M of absolute space lying at equal absolute distances from the places P and Q of absolute space in which these two events occur. For, if these two events are then observed simultaneously in M, one can justly say that they occur at the same time. However, these definitions do not have any *physical* sense unless one can experimentally determine those absolutely immobile reference points, i.e., unless one can experimentally determine one's own motion with respect to these absolutely immobile points.

On the basis of electrodynamic views, classical physics thought that it had found such an absolute frame of description in the ether. The question, however, was whether it would be possible to verify the existence of absolute motion with respect to that absolutely motionless ether. Maxwell devised an experiment to settle this issue, but when Michelson and Morley succeeded in performing it, no positive result was reached.[89]

The third solution was that proposed by Einstein's ideas concerning time and space. We will devote the following chapter to it.

---

[89] Poincaré, *op. cit.,* pp. 45-48; Bridgman, *op. cit.,* pp. 7-9; Einstein, *The Meaning of Relativity,* pp. 14-15, 26-27. See also above, pp. 103-110.

CHAPTER EIGHT

EINSTEIN'S IDEAS CONCERNING TIME AND SPACE

1. The Starting Point of the Theory of Relativity

Rejection of Unverifiable Absolutes. When the experiments of Michelson and Morley produced no positive results, a decision imposed itself. Physical science could obstinately hold on to the classical ideas concerning space, time, place, length, duration, simultaneity at a distance, and similar notions as *absolute* data and then try to explain those experiments through supplementary hypotheses. Or it could take the experimental results as the basis on which those ideas would be given a new, experimentally verifiable content. Differently expressed, a choice had to be made between making new artificial postulates or abandoning arbitrary postulates.

FitzGerald and Lorentz opted for the first alternative.[90] They held fast to the classical conceptions of space, time, and motion and endeavored to explain the experimental facts by means of their so-called theory of contraction. According to that theory, the length of a body contracts in the direction of its motion proportionally to the square of its velocity.[91] Moreover, they added the hypothesis that clocks go slower proportionally to the square of the velocity which they have in an absolute frame of description. On the basis of these hypotheses, it is possible to explain the experimental facts, at least if the contraction of length and the deceleration are calculated by the Lorentz transformations. The disadvantage of this solution is that the absolute time and space to which the theory holds fast cannot be experimentally observed, since the measuring instruments of space and time are subject to the same contraction and deceleration. Ultimately, therefore, the theory amounts

---

[90] Others also, such as Ritz and La Rosa, at first sought the answer in this direction. Cf. Selvaggi, "Assoluto e relativo nel tempo," *Gregorianum,* vol. 28, p. 342.

[91] For a more profound explanation of this contraction theory these authors appeal to Lorentz' theory of electrons. Cf. Bavink, *op. cit.,* p. 103.

to the acceptance of absolute space and time as fundamental postulates but in such a way that they are not *physically* observable. To make those postulates acceptable, bodies would have to lose their rigid and invariable firmness and seconds would be deprived of their univocal meaning.[92]

Einstein[93] found it unreasonable to speak of unobservable absolutes and demanded that here also the relevant physical quantities be submitted to the requirements of the operational method. He wanted to admit as physical quantities only that which can be defined in terms of a process of measurement.[94] Since, then, the experiments which, according to the views of the classical theory, should have produced positive results, led only to *negative* results, one had to conclude that the postulated *absolute* space and time, physically speaking, do not possess any accurately circumscribed sense. Thus, it followed that the classical definitions of both isochronism and synchronism were no longer tenable.[95]

The Necessity of New Definitions of Spatial and Temporal Quantities. We, therefore, face the task of giving a new physical content to those concepts. First, however, we must reflect on the problem of

---

[92] For the solution offered by Lorentz and his followers see Fokker, *Filosofie in de natuurkunde,* p. 99; Eddington, *Space, Time and Gravitation,* pp. 17-29; *The Nature of the Physical World,* pp. 1-12.

[93] When here and elsewhere we name Einstein, we want to include not only the father of the theory of relativity but also the work done by many other mathematicians and physicists who have influenced this theory. Of these we may name Mach, Poincaré, Lorentz, Whittaker, FitzGerald, Larmor, Voigt, Minkowski, Ricci, Levi-Civita, Ritz, La Rosa, Weyl, Eddington, Born, von Kaluza, Schouten, Friedmann, Lemaître, de Sitter, Fokker, Klein, Veblen, Schrödinger, Hlavaty, Kohler, Jonsson, Bergman, and Jordan. Cf. Bavink, *op. cit.,* pp. 100-137; Swanenburg, *op. cit.,* pp. 275-280; Jordan, *Schwerkraft und Weltall, passim;* Eddington, *Space, Time and Gravitation,* pp. 210-213; Dampier, *A History of Science* . . . , pp. 399-410.

[94] Bridgman, *The Logic of Modern Physics,* pp. 1-2, 3-9; Renoirte, *art. cit.* in footnote 19, p. 275. The assertion that the physicist wants to accept only that which can be defined through a process of measurement does not exclude the admission of hypotheses and axioms. Einstein himself continues to hold fast to two presuppositions, namely, that the velocity of light in a vacuum is constant in all directions, independently of the chosen frame of reference, and that the classical principle of relativity is valid also for electromagnetic phenomena. The general theory of relativity only enlarges the second principle. However, this point need not concern us here. Cf., e.g., Seiler, *Philosophie der unbelebten Natur,* pp. 137-139; van Melsen, *Science and Technology,* Pittsburgh, 1961, pp. 190-191; Einstein, *The Meaning of Relativity,* pp. 25-27; Einstein and Infeld, *op. cit.,* pp. 184-186; Born, *art. cit.* in footnote 17, pp. 249-250.

[95] Bridgman, *op. cit.,* pp. 68-69, 73-74.

measuring distances, because the solution of that problem is presupposed by the definition of simultaneity at a distance.

Einstein demands, moreover, that the new definitions of spatial and temporal quantities result in *invariable* metric numbers since, as we have seen, the admission of privileged frames of reference cannot be based on any objective grounds.[96] For, the new physical quantities also will have to be defined in terms of the measuring process through which measured numbers will be obtained. And if one claims that these numbers change when the frames of reference change, then either one will get another number than that expected or such a number does not exist at all. But if the number is the same, it is meaningless to speak of a change of metric numbers since there would be no number with respect to which that change could be *physically* verified. Perhaps all this can be more clearly expressed by saying that all metric numbers are *relative* to the frame of reference in which they were obtained.

The question of how, nonetheless, the results of measurements can be invariable with respect to a change of standpoint is a point that can better be discussed later. Otherwise, we would anticipate the solution offered by Einstein and Minkowski.[97]

2. Einstein's Idea of the Measurement of Length[98]

No one will have difficulty in understanding that the number of objects pertaining to a certain collection of things may be called an *absolute* quantity. Such a number can usually be verified by direct counting, but sometimes this absolute datum can be verified only indirectly. In both cases, however, it is true that the number of those objects pertaining to that collection cannot be dependent on the method used to determine that number exactly. For this reason counting is always said to be an absolute operation.[99]

Length, on the contrary, is not a pure number but a physical quantity whose definition consists of describing the measuring process through which one is led to assign a certain metric number to a certain length.

---

[96] Renoirte, *art. cit.,* pp. 275-276; Einstein and Infeld, *op. cit.,* pp. 220-225. See also above, pp. 121-125.

[97] See below, pp. 138-150.

[98] For what follows see Renoirte, *art. cit.,* pp. 281-291; Bridgman, *op. cit.,* pp. 9-25; Einstein and Infeld, *op. cit.,* pp. 186-202; and the references given below.

[99] Carnap, *op. cit.,* pp. 14-16; Eddington, *The Mathematical Theory . . . ,* p. 5; *The Nature of the Physical World,* pp. 23-27; Renoirte, *art. cit.,* p. 281.

If, for example, one says that a stick is five feet long, he really wants to say that a certain procedure has been applied to this physical system in such a way that it resulted in the metric number "five." The question now is whether this reply supplies us with fully objective information regarding that physical system. Can we say unqualifiedly that length is an absolute magnitude?

"Proper-Length." To find the answer to that question, we have to enter into greater detail. Let us, therefore, briefly analyze a very simple case. We assume that we have some perceptible object, let us say a stick; that we have a measuring rod whose length by definition is one foot; that the rules governing the use of this rod have been fixed; and that, by putting the rod alongside the stick as required by the rules, we have arrived at the conclusion that the length of the stick is five feet. In that case what we really want to assert is that we have five times performed a certain operation. Five, as we have seen, is an absolute quantity, but the operation in question is meaningful only within the physical experiment we have made. The truth of this assertion is evident as soon as we recall that, by following the rule of placing the rod alongside the stick, we have tacitly tied our operation to a frame of reference in which the object to be measured is at rest. When the "length" of a physical system is determined by bringing a measuring instrument into contact with it, then we are said to determine the "proper-length" of this system.[100]

Length of a Moving Body. It may happen that the proper-length of a certain system cannot be directly determined, for instance, if that object is far away from our measuring instrument or if it is in motion with respect to our instrument. In that case we have to make use of a different measuring process. This process, however, cannot lead us to the proper-length of that system, for we are then making use of a different process from the one through which we have defined proper-length. In other words, we are *not* making use of the measuring process by which proper-length is defined. Nevertheless, that which is being measured is a physical quantity, a quantity, therefore, that is to be determined by the process through which it is being measured. Of

---

[100] Concerning the meaning of the term "proper-length" see Eddington, *The Nature of the Physical World*, pp. 23-27; *Space, Time and Gravitation*, p. 11, *The Mathematical Theory* . . . , pp. 34, 80-81. On page 34 of the last-named work he says: "Quantities referred to the space-time system of an observer moving with the body considered are often distinguished by the prefix *proper-* (German *Eigen-*), e.g., proper-length, proper-volume, proper-density, proper-mass-invariant mass."

course, this process also constitutes a physical experience for us, just as well as the process mentioned above in connection with the measurement of the proper-length of the stick.   But also this experience is not fully characterized as long as one cannot state exactly all the physical conditions in which it takes place.   If these conditions change, then our physical experience also changes and, therefore, possibly the metric number attained through it.

Let us assume now that we have two observers possessing exactly the same measuring instruments.   By "exactly the same measuring instruments" we mean here that, if one is put on top of the other, they have the same proper-length.   We assume also that both observers use their instruments in exactly the same way and that both make observations of the same object.   If these two observers now move with different velocities in reference to that object, then they are, with respect to that physical system, in different physical situations and therefore have different experiences.   In such a case it is not *a priori* excluded that they will not arrive at the same metric number in measuring the length of this physical system.

Nevertheless, it should be clear that the system to be observed does not assume a different form when it is perceived by an observer for whom it has velocity *a* from the form it has when it is perceived by an observer for whom it has velocity *b*.   Hence the problem here is not *how* the *material objects* change within absolute space (Lorentz' contraction), but rather of determining as exactly as possible *what* has been measured in each of those experiences and then to define what relation exists between the change in the discovered results and the change in the physical way of measuring.[101]

The measuring of the length of a body which is at rest with respect to the measuring rod is an extremely simple process, once the rod has been defined and the rules for its use have been fixed.   But the problem becomes quite different when one of the two is in motion with respect to the other.   On this point Einstein breaks away from classical physics. The classical theory has recourse here to postulates, which is precisely what Einstein wants to avoid.[102]

Einstein begins by asking himself what exactly is meant when we speak about the *length* of a *moving body*.   That expression also

---

[101] For this whole matter see Renoirte, *art. cit.,* pp. 281-286.

[102] For the meaning of this "hypothesis of equivalence" see Fokker, *Relativiteitstheorie,* pp. 196-198.

obviously refers to the result of a physical experience. Let us consider such an experience and assume that one could indicate two points at rest which would be passed *at the same time* by the beginning and the end of the body to be measured. In that case, one could say, I could determine the length of that body by measuring the distance between those two points. What I find then will be the proper-length of the line connecting those two points, which are at rest in my frame of description. But I do not find the proper-length of the body to be measured. Of course, one could object: But the extremes of that body were *at the same time* in those two points; therefore, I have the proper-length of the body. That raises the question of what exactly is meant by the expression *"at the same time."*[103]

3. Einstein's Definition of Simultaneity[104]

Necessity of a Definition of Simultaneity. It is necessary, therefore, to give a definition of simultaneity. As we have indicated above, with respect to distant events the concept of simultaneity, physically speaking, cannot be said to be a primary datum of experience. For, we have immediate knowledge only of things with which we are in immediate spatio-temporal contact. With regard to events that are spatio-temporally distant from us, we know only that those events are exterior to us and that we will learn about them only after a certain lapse of time. To be able to speak in more precise quantitative terms about the exteriority of two events, we need, as we have seen, a definition of simultaneity. However, in physical science the concept of simultaneity is meaningful only within the framework of a physical experience through which we can verify the simultaneous character of two events. Moreover, the physicist's desire for *objective* certainty and truth requires that the personal views of the observers be eliminated as much as possible. In other words, the definition we would like to find should describe an experience that is independent of any frame of description.

Simultaneity and Frame of Reference. Classical mechanics thought that an absolute sense could be given to the concept of simultaneity on the basis of the existence of absolute time. Einstein, however, rejected all uncontrollable absolutes and demanded that simultaneity be exactly

---

[103] Renoirte, *art. cit.,* pp. 286-288.

[104] For what follows cf. especially Renoirte, *art. cit.,* pp. 288-291; Bridgman, *op. cit.,* pp. 7-9; Einstein and Infeld, *op. cit.,* pp. 186-202.

defined in such a way that one indicates the process through which the definition can be exactly verified. To clarify the matter, let us take two points A and B, both situated in a certain frame of reference at rest. Connecting the two points by a straight line, we get a line having an invariable length and a center M. Let us now imagine that in M there is an observer equipped with two mirrors for receiving light signals from A and B. In *this* frame of description we say that the events A and B are simultaneous by *definition* if the light signals sent from A and B can be perceived as simultaneous in M. Differently expressed, we define the temporal co-incidence of two distant events through the spatio-temporal coincidence of two other events. On the basis of this definition one can unambiguously speak of simultaneity, but this definition is meaningful *only* within the particular frame of description we selected.[105]

If we apply these ideas to the length measurement of a particular physical system which moves with respect to that frame of description, then we must say that the length of that system is equal to the proper-length of the straight line connecting the two points which are at rest *in our descriptive frame* and through which the extremes of the system to be measured passed simultaneously *in our* descriptive frame. We have no right, of course, to claim that this statement, divorced from that descriptive frame, would have an unambiguous sense. Hence, the metric number, in itself, does not supply us with any wholly objective datum concerning the body in question. For this reason we should not be surprised if another metric number was found in reference to another descriptive frame which with respect to the system to be

---

[105] Absolutely speaking, i.e., abstracting from this or that particular frame of description, the events A and B cannot be called simultaneous. With A. Robb, *Geometry of Time and Space,* Cambridge, 1936, pp. 1-25, one can say that they are neither-before-nor-after.

Robb, moreover, judges it incorrect to speak of simultaneity within a particular frame of description if there is question of events at a distance. Here, too, he would prefer to speak of neither-before-nor-after. He concludes his critique of Einstein's terminology by saying: "It is perhaps desirable to point out that it is Einstein's philosophy which I am here attacking and not his mathematics" (*op. cit.,* pp. 11-13). Although there is much to be said in favor of Robb's standpoint, we will follow here and throughout this study the current, though less accurate, terminology. The relativation of simultaneity, spoken of here, implies, of course, also an analogous relativation of anteriority and posteriority, as well as a relativation of the time measures between two events. However, we need not consider them here because they lie beyond the scope of the present argument. Cf. Selvaggi, "Assoluto e relativo nel tempo," *Gregorianum,* vol. 28, pp. 342-346.

measured was in a different state of motion. Neither one nor the other result is false; they are simply different. The term "length" itself has become ambiguous in the sense that we can never speak of length without further qualification, but have to speak about the length of a particular body in this or that frame of description. The determination of length, like that of simultaneity, is, physically speaking, something relative.

4. The Measurement of Time.   Relativity of Space and Time

Before we consider the problem of measuring time intervals, it may be useful to summarize the results attained in the preceding pages and express them succinctly in a few definitions.

Definitions. By "measuring rod" of lengths we mean a particular, arbitrarily chosen physical system. This system is preserved in the same physical conditions at Sèvres, near Paris. It is called the "meter."

The "proper-length" of any other physical system is measured by bringing that meter successively in contact with this system so that its full length is covered by this system. Instead of using the Sèvres meter, one may also use, of course, another measuring rod that has been checked against that meter. But in that case one has to take into account possible changes resulting from differences in temperature, pressure, and other factors. This definition indicates implicitly that the proper-length of a body which is in motion with respect to our measuring rod cannot be determined.

Two events A and B, occurring at points P and Q of our descriptive frame, are said to be "simultaneous with respect to our frame of reference" if light rays from these events are perceived at the same time at point C of this frame of reference, provided that this point is equidistant from points P and Q in this same frame. This definition, then, is relative to the chosen frame of reference. Nevertheless, it has objective value, for the definition makes use only of distances within the same system whose proper-length can be verified absolutely and, in addition, avoids a vicious circular definition because the expression "at the same time" is not taken in a physical sense but in a psychical sense.[106]

To measure the "length of a system" in motion with respect to the

---

[106] See, however, also the preceding footnote.

measuring rod, we have first to determine two points *P* and *Q* in our frame of reference in which the extremes of the system to be measured are at the same time, provided this simultaneity is determined, as above, with respect to this same descriptive system. The measurement of the straight line between *P* and *Q* of this descriptive system results in the length of the system-in-motion with respect to the chosen descriptive system. By a "straight line" we mean here the shortest possible connection between the two relevant points of the descriptive frame.

Measurement of Time Intervals. Applying these data to the measurement of temporal durations, we will first have to define a measuring instrument. We do this in the following way. Any observer has an intuitive knowledge of the order of time on the basis of which he can say that *A* occurs before *B* and *C* before *D*. This intuitive knowledge, however, has no quantitative value in most cases, so that one cannot simply assert that the time interval between *A* and *B* is exactly equal to that between *C* and *D*. A clock is needed to measure this quantitative aspect in an exact way. By a "clock" we mean "a mechanism of some sort in which a certain process is repeated over and over under the same conditions as far as possible." Any oscillating system is such a mechanism to a greater or lesser extent. By idealizing such a mechanism, one arrives at a so-called "ideal clock," of which it is accepted that the intervals between the various periods are of exactly equal duration.[107]

The proper-time of a series of events is found when the duration of this series is measured with a clock which coincides in a spatio-temporal way with this series. Again, this assertion implicitly contains the admission that the proper-time of a series of events which is in motion with respect to the clock cannot be determined through this clock.[108]

---

[107] Einstein and Infeld, *op. cit.*, pp. 188-189; Einstein, *The Meaning of Relativity*, pp. 1, 34-35; Synge, *op. cit.*, pp. 14-15; Bridgman, *op. cit.*, pp. 69-73, 176-177. Bridgman raises here several difficulties against Einstein's view, but, in our opinion, he wants to interpret the operational method too rigorously. Cf. also C. Møller, "The Ideal Standard Clocks in the General Theory of Relativity," *Fünfzig Jahre Relativitätstheorie,* Basel, 1956, pp. 54-57; A. J. Garrat, "The National Physical Laboratory. Open Days," *Nature,* vol. 178 (1956), pp. 166-168; L. Essen, "Atomic Time and the Definition of the Second," *ibid.,* pp. 34-35; Fokker, "Accelerated Spherical Light Wave Clocks in Chronogeometry," *Verhandelingen v.d. Koninklijke Akademie van Wetenschappen,* vol. 59 (1956), pp. 451-454.

[108] For this whole matter see Renoirte, *art. cit.,* pp. 292-293; Bridgman, *op. cit.,* pp. 68-69.

The question now is how one can verify that two clocks, situated at a certain distance from each other, indicate exactly the same time. Einstein proposes the following solution. First, one determines the center *M* of the straight line connecting the two clocks. If, next, we telecast pictures of both clocks and in these pictures the clocks run exactly equal, two of these pictures will reach me in *M* at the same time. However, the expression "at the same time" has no absolute value, but, as we have seen, is valid only within the chosen frame of reference. If, now, the two clocks always indicate exactly the same time in *M,* then we say that they are perfectly synchronized *within our descriptive frame.*

In an analogous fashion one can exactly determine the duration of a series of events at a distance by means of a single clock. Since in this case also the concept of simultaneity plays an essential role, this definition has no absolute value but applies only *within the frame of reference that we have chosen.* The same must be said with respect to a series of events which is in motion in reference to the chosen descriptive frame.[109]

Relativity of Simultaneity and Reciprocity. With Einstein, we have learned to take a critical view of certain fundamental definitions of classical physics. He demands that they be reformulated in strictly verifiable terms and does not want to appeal to physically unknowable absolutes. The new formulations always refer to a particular descriptive frame, although they can be formulated analogously in any Galileo system;[110] hence the new formulations have only a *relative* value. Consequently, it is not at all a contradiction to assert that events which are simultaneous with respect to one frame of reference will *not* be simultaneous with respect to another frame of reference which is in motion in relation to the first frame. For, the concept of simultaneity of distant events can be defined only with respect to a certain frame of description. Analogous considerations apply to the other quantities.

From these assertions it also follows that observers in different systems of reference who do not arrive at the same results with respect to the simultaneity or non-simultaneity of two events happening at a distance from each other are not in contradiction but concerned with different physical realities. It is important in this matter, however, that both observers express themselves always in reciprocal statements.

To clarify this point, let us assume that we have two descriptive

---

[109] Einstein and Infeld, *op. cit.,* p. 189. However, see also footnote 105.

[110] In the general theory of relativity this rule applies even to all frames of reference. Cf., e.g., Einstein, *The Meaning of Relativity,* pp. 54-60.

frames which are in uniform rectilinear motion with respect to each other. Let us assume, further, that in one system (A) a certain complex of events is described in a set of statements S_A and that this same complex of events is described in the other system (B) in a set of statements T_B. If now another complex of events is described in system B in a set of statements S_B, then the observer in system A will have to describe this same complex in a set of statements T_B (if the sign indicating velocity occurs, it has to be changed).

If these assertions are correct, then it should be evident that from the metric numbers obtained by an observer in system A one can *per se* calculate the metric numbers which an observer in the other frame of description B should find. From the mathematical viewpoint Lorentz had already expressed this reciprocity in his new transformation formulae. It was not difficult for Einstein to demonstrate how those formulae are in full agreement with the new physical definitions which he had formulated.

5. *The Doctrine of Absolute Relations*

Einstein was fully aware of the fact that the new view did not have only advantages and no drawbacks. True, by applying the operational method also to lengths and time intervals, the physicist henceforth knew exactly what he was speaking about when he referred to one of those quantities. The drawback, however, was that, instead of having the old absolutes, he had to be satisfied now with merely relative metric numbers.[111] Thus, it was only natural that the question was asked whether no absolute metric numbers at all can be found. Will we always have to limit ourselves to saying: with respect to this descriptive frame the matter is this, and with respect to that other frame it is that? In their search for an answer, the "relativists" permitted themselves be led by the following consideration.

The Denial of Two Absolute Relations of Space and Time. If we want to indicate a particular, really existing physical system in an unambiguous fashion, then we must be able to indicate at least that it is

---

[111] Hence the theory of relativity never speaks about the relativity of so-called world conditions. It recognizes these conditions as absolute, but speaks only about the relativity of physical quantities, i.e., the relativity of the metric numbers of these absolute world conditions. Cf. Eddington, *The Mathematical Theory* . . . , pp. 1-7; *The Nature of the Physical World*, pp. 23-27.

at this particular place at this particular moment. In other words, for an unambiguous determination of a physical reality a spatio-temporal definition is necessary. The trouble, however, is that physical realities have a continuous duration, and to define a perduring reality unambiguously is an exceedingly complex task. Even when there is question only of a point and a *now* of time, it is not easy to give an unambiguous and objective description. The most simple case seems to be that of the point-event, which can be unambiguously determined by means of four co-ordinates.[112] Let us explain the matter somewhat more in detail.

By an "event" we mean here anything that can happen.[113] A "point-event" is obtained as the limit of events conceived to be increasingly smaller; this limit is no longer spatially or temporally extended. The totality of all events constitutes a four-dimensional continuum, which is called "space-time."[114] By saying that our space-time is four-dimensional, we admit that any point-event in this space-time can be unambiguously determined only through four numbers. These numbers, x_1, x_2, x_3, and x_4, are called the "co-ordinates" of this point-event in space-time.[115] As Carnap has shown, these definitions themselves remain fully within the domain of classical physics. However, one would look in vain for such formulations in classical treatises, because they did not feel the need for those kinds of considerations.[116] Classical physics was used to split those four co-ordinates into three Cartesian co-ordinates, *x, y, z,* and the so-called time *t* of Newton. Thus, it tacitly postulated that between every two point-events there must exist *two* absolute and independent metric relations, viz., the metric number of their spatial exteriority and the metric number of their temporal exteriority. This postulate was based on the existence of absolute space and time and

---

[112] On the other hand, an analytic representation by means of co-ordinates is not essential, although it would be the most simple representation in a physical theory. Cf. Eddington, *The Mathematical Theory* . . . , pp. 8-9; see also Robb, *op. cit.*

[113] Synge, *op. cit.*, p. 5. For a critique of such a definition see Bridgman, *op. cit.*, pp. 167-178. Here, too, Bridgman's interpretation of the operational method seems to be too rigorous.

[114] Synge, *op. cit.*, p. 6.; A. Alexandrov, "The Space-Time of the Theory of Relativity," *Fünfzig Jahre Relativitätstheorie*, pp. 44-45; Eddington, *Space, Time and Gravitation*, pp. 77-92; *The Nature of the Physical World*, pp. 36-62; Weyl, *Philosophy of Mathematics and Natural Science*, pp. 95-138; Einstein, *The Meaning of Relativity*, pp. 28-31; Beth, *Natuurphilosophie*, p. 155.

[115] Synge, *op. cit.*, p. 6.

[116] Carnap, *op. cit.*, p. 55; Einstein, *op. cit.*, p. 29; Einstein and Infeld, *op. cit.*, pp. 217-219.

their reciprocal independence. But a "relativist," as we have seen, does not define his quantities by postulating absolutes but by describing the measuring processes through which these quantities are to be measured. He therefore protests against the classical view in a twofold way, for he refuses to speak of quantities that cannot be defined by the operational method and he denies the existence of physical quantities that are *not* supposed to be defined with the aid of a certain descriptive frame, *at least as long as* one remains within the confines of classical physics.

The Affirmation of One Absolute Relation of Interval. All this, however, does not deny the existence of every absolute relation. Einstein's provisional conclusion simply is that classical physics was on the wrong track. For, if absolute space and absolute time are *physically* unacceptable because they are not verifiable, then it is, *physically* speaking, unreasonable also to detach a three-dimensional spatial continuum in the four-dimensional space-time continuum from Newton's time dimension and to make this time a fourth independent variable.[117] In this way the postulate that between two point-events there must exist *two* absolute and independent relations is dropped. It appears now more likely that between two events there exists only one independent and absolute relation. The question, however, is how this relation is to be discovered.

The first thing to do is to describe some kind of experiment through which, at least in principle, an exact bond can be established between a particular point-event and the four co-ordinates (x_1, x_2, x_3, x_4) of physical space-time. Now if a certain point-event has been defined by co-ordinates in two different experiments, then these co-ordinates will, as a rule, not be the same. If, then, in this way two series of co-ordinates, x_1, x_2, x_3, x_4, and y_1, y_2, y_3, y_4, have been found, at least formulae for the transformation of co-ordinates like the following must apply to them:

---

[117] Accordingly, the separation which classical physics makes between space and time is merely one of innumerable possibilities. Any other particular frame of description makes such an arbitrary "cut" through this four-dimensional continuum (cf. Fokker, *Relativiteitstheorie,* pp. 53-57).

Nevertheless, the theory of relativity always speaks of a $(3 + 1)$-dimensional continuum, or even more clearly, of a $(3 + 1)$-dimensional space-time, because it does not at all intend to make the spatial and temporal dimension equal in all respects. Cf. Einstein, *The Meaning of Relativity,* pp. 28-29; Einstein and Infeld, *op. cit.,* pp. 217-219.

Finally, one could ask what could possibly be the meaning of a $(4 + 0)$- or of a $(2 + 2)$-dimensional continuum. Cf. Eddington, *The Mathematical Theory . . . ,* p. 25.

$$x_1 = x_1 \ (y_1, \ y_2, \ y_3, \ y_4)$$
$$x_2 = x_2 \ (y_1, \ y_2, \ y_3, \ y_4)$$
$$x_3 = x_3 \ (y_1, \ y_2, \ y_3, \ y_4)$$
$$x_4 = x_4 \ (y_1, \ y_2, \ y_3, \ y_4)^{118} \qquad (1)$$

We assume, in addition, that by a "material particle" is meant a *moving* point with which we connect certain numbers to indicate its mass, charge, etc.[119] The history of such a particle consists of a continuous series of events and this series can be mathematically indicated in four equations. Geometrically, therefore, we are entitled to conceive the history of that material particle as a curve in space-time. Such a curve is called the "world line" of this particle.[120]

An observer likewise may be conceived as a material particle describing a certain world line. And we accept that an observer can arrange the events on *his* world line unambiguously. For instance, for two given events on his world line he can unambiguously indicate that this one event occurred before that other. With respect to the events occurring on his world line, therefore, he can distinguish between past, future, and present.[121] Hence we accept an intrinsic order of time, but add at once the restriction that this order is valid *only* for the events occurring on the observer's world line. Thus, we drop the Newtonian idea of time.[122]

Let us assume now that an observer takes a standard clock with him along his world line from event A to event B. Assuming, moreover, that this clock indicates in A the time S_A and in B the time S_B, then we will call $S = S_B - S_A$ the "exteriority" between A and B, measured along the world line in question. If A lies close to B, then this exteriority becomes infinitesimal, and is indicated as ds. Now, ds is a function of the co-ordinates of A and B. Calling these co-ordinates x and $x + dx$, we can write:

$$ds = f \ (x, dx).^{123} \qquad (2)$$

---

[118] Synge, *op. cit.*, pp. 7-8.
[119] Synge, *ibid.*, p. 5.
[120] Synge, *ibid.*, pp. 9-10.
[121] Synge, *ibid.*, pp. 10-11.
[122] Synge, *ibid.*, pp. 11-12.
[123] Synge, *ibid.*, p. 15.

If we want to arrive at a physical theory that can be verified by experiments, we must try to specify the function f (x, dx) for one or other system of co-ordinates. As should be clear, there exists a certain exteriority between events which occur in close proximity without, however, coinciding. Since these events are real, this exteriority is a real exteriority. It stands to reason, moreover, that this exteriority has a certain *absolute* magnitude. On the basis of our experience in simple mathematics, it stands to reason also that the above-mentioned relation may be replaced by the following equation:

$$ds^2 = g_{11}dx_1{}^2 + g_{22}dx_2{}^2 + g_{33}dx_3{}^2 + g_{44}dx_4{}^2 + 2g_{12}dx_1dx_2 + 2g_{13}dx_1dx_3$$
$$+ 2g_{14}dx_1dx_4 + 2g_{23}dx_2dx_3 + 2g_{24}dx_2dx_4 + 2g_{34}dx_3dx_4. ^{124} \qquad (3)$$

Or, expressed in tensor notation[125]:

$$ds^2 = g_{mn}dx_mdx_n. ^{126} \qquad (4)$$

Although this formula has been derived by starting from a temporal exteriority, no reason can be given why it would not be valid also for a spatial exteriority, since the formula in question should hold everywhere in that area. At first, we know only *particular* components, dx_1, dx_2, dx_3, dx_4. If the formula is to have *universal* validity, it may not be dependent on components which somehow depend on the standpoint of the observer.[127] Only in that case do we have an *absolute* relation between two close point-events, having as their co-ordinates (x_1, x_2, x_3, x_4) and ($x_1 + dx_1$, $x_2 + dx_2$, $x_3 + dx_3$, $x_4 + dx_4$).

Accordingly, if one says that between two given points there exists this

---

[124] Eddington, *op. cit.*, pp. 10-11; *Space, Time and Gravitation*, pp. 77-84. For a more general consideration of this problem see Synge, *op. cit.*, pp. 16-34.

[125] Concerning the nature and meaning of the tensor calculus see Einstein, *The Meaning of Relativity*, pp. 62-63; Eddington, *The Mathematical Theory . . .*, pp. 2-3, 8-11, 68, 111-112. For a brief survey of the most important equations and operations of the tensor calculus see Margenau and G. Murphy, *The Mathematics of Physics and Chemistry*, New York, 1953, pp. 156-166; Fokker, *Relativiteitstheorie*, pp. 95-112; Eddington, *The Mathematical Theory . . .*, pp. 43-75; Synge and A. Schild, *Tensor Calculus*, Toronto, 1952.

[126] Synge, *op. cit.*, pp. 22-24.

[127] This statement implies that the theory of relativity does not recognize any privileged frame of description. For the consequences of this standpoint see Eddington, *The Mathematical Theory . . .*, pp. 8-10; *The Nature of the Physical World*, pp. 1-35 (*passim*); Einstein, *The Meaning of Relativity*, pp. 54-60.

or that *spatial* distance, one has always to add: in this or that frame of reference. The same applies to any particular *temporal* distance between two particular moments. But if one says that this or that *interval*[128] exists between two point-events, then this statement is *absolute* and independent of any descriptive frame whatsoever. Generally speaking, therefore, we may say that a law of nature based only on such intervals is an absolute law.[129]

"Geometric" Examples Illustrating the Meaning of the Absolute Relation. Obviously, with this interval relation we have only reached the beginning of the theory of relativity. The formula of the intervals contains factors g_{mn}, which are technically called "tensors." These fundamental tensors and others that can be derived from them supply the theory with a means to formulate the known laws of physics on an absolute basis. We cannot enter into details here concerning the way it is done but refer the reader to the appropriate treatises.[130] However, it may be useful to illustrate the meaning of absolute relations through a few "geometric" examples.

To keep the examples as simple as possible, we will limit ourselves to a single spatial co-ordinate (X) rather than using all three. In this way we will be able to represent spatio-temporal relations between events in a two-dimensional figure. We will call this figure an XT-*diagram*, because we will represent spatial distances on the X-axis and temporal distances on the T-axis. Our XT-diagram, then, is a two-dimensional continuum but not an ordinary spatial plane. Fokker calls such an improper plane an "enduring straight line," since the figure wants to indicate that the "straight line," chosen as spatial X-axis, endures in the time indicated by the T-axis.

---

[128] "In four-dimensional space-time there is likewise a certain extension or generalized distance between two events, of which the distance in space and the separation in time are particular components. This extension in space and time combined is called "the interval" between the two events; it is the same for all observers, however they resolve it into space and time separately." Eddington, *Space, Time and Gravitation*, pp. 45-46. Cf. also *The Mathematical Theory* . . . , pp. 9-10; Fokker, *Relativiteitstheorie*, pp. 28-29, 47-48, 84-85; Synge, *op. cit.*, pp. 15-16, 22-26, 38-42, 56-58.

[129] Later it became apparent that the interval could not be a *fundamental* concept. Cf. Eddington, *The Mathematical Theory* . . . , pp. 196-237; *Space, Time and Gravitation*, pp. 167-177; Jordan, *Schwerkraft und Weltall, passim.* For our argument here, however, this point is not important, as is explained by Eddington, *loc. cit.*

[130] Cf., e.g., Eddington, *The Mathematical Theory* . . . ; Fokker, *op. cit.*; Synge, *op. cit.*, and the references given by them.

If in this improper plane we draw arbitrary straight or curved "lines," these lines represent motions of a spatially non-extended entity. These lines are world lines, but, with Fokker, one could call them "time tracks." A time track which is a straight line represents a motion having a *uniform* velocity. A straight time track perpendicular to the X-axis indicates the duration of something which is spatially standing still, while a horizontal straight line represents that a great number of events occur at the same time; in both cases these statements are meant to refer to a *particular* descriptive frame. In other words, relations of "one after the other" are indicated in the vertical direction in the XT-diagram, and relations of "one alongside the other," in the horizontal direction.

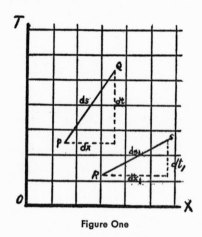

Figure One

The XT-diagram may be divided into small squares by means of horizontal and vertical lines, drawn at equal distances from one another and from the X and T axes (see Figure One). Now if we take two arbitrary point-events P and Q in our diagram, representing two arbitrary point-events of reality, one would be inclined to think that the distance ds between these points can be expressed in the following equation by means of the theorem of Pythagoras:

$$ds^2 = dx^2 + dt^2, \qquad (5)$$

in which formula dx and dt represent the components of the interval.

But in that case he forgets that we do not have to do here with ordinary geometry. In our "geometry" time also plays a role, and for this reason, as we have already noted, one could best speak here with Fokker about "chronogeometry."[131]   In this chronogeometry, as a rule, entirely different theorems apply from those valid for Euclidean space geometry.   For instance, the above-mentioned equation (5) will have to be replaced by the chronogeometric equation:

$$ds^2 = dt^2 - dx^2 \qquad (6)$$

which could be called the improper theorem of Pythagoras for this improper plane.   The minus sign in this equation is very important, for it expresses that a length is not a temporal duration.   It is important also to note that the magnitude of the interval between the two real events represented by the two point-events P and Q is not at all expressed by the magnitude of the line drawn in the figure.

Because of the minus sign before dx^2 there can be two kinds of intervals. ds^2 can be positive, namely, if dt is greater than dx; in that case the interval expresses a *temporal duration* and one of the events situated at the extreme of the interval comes after the other.   But it may also happen that dx is greater than dt; in that case ds^2 is negative and the interval then has the value of a *spatial distance;* the one extreme is neither before nor after the other but only *alongside* the other.   There is even a borderline case in which ds is neither positive nor negative but zero.   This case can be represented by two straight lines passing through the origin (O) of the XT-diagram and forming 45° angles with the X-axis (see Figure Two).[132]   For reasons which will become clear later we will call these lines "asymptotes."   In this figure the temporal durations resulting from events of the past and going to events of the future pass through origin O of *Figure Two,* provided the lines representing these temporal durations remain inside the asymptotes.   Genuine spatial distances lie between O and the events which remain to the left and to the right of O inside the asymptotes.   The events in quadrant A are future with respect to the event represented by O; the events in B are past in reference to O; and the events in C and D occur elsewhere, not-here.   Events lying on the asymptotes are, with respect to O, neither past nor future, they do neither occur elsewhere.   Their interval to O is zero.

---

[131] Fokker, "Over de absoluta der chronogeometrie," *art. cit.* in footnote 8, p. 133.

[132] Cf. Robb, *Geometry of Time and Space,* pp. 1-3; Eddington, *The Mathematical Theory* . . . , pp. 13-16, 22-23.

Strictly speaking, they constitute, together with the event in *O,* a single "here-now." For this reason Fokker prefers to call the asymptotes "here-now radii." Between two events lying on the same asymptote there is, as we have said, a zero interval. Such a zero distance could be called a *telethigma,*[133] a "touching at a distance."

The *XT*-diagram divided into small squares (see Figure One) represents, as we have seen, the descriptive frame of an observer who is

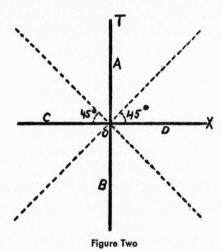

Figure Two

at rest with respect to that frame. We may now ask ourselves how we should divide the *XT*-diagram for an observer who moves with a uniform motion with respect to this frame of reference. We can begin by pointing out that the ascending lines in the new frame of reference will have to be straight oblique lines. The angle *a* which these lines make with the *X*-axis is determined by the velocity of the observer. The question, however, is how the other two sides of the old squares are to be drawn. At first, one could think that they should be drawn in such a way that squares will again be formed (see Figure Three). But that is impossible. For, by continuing the turn, one would ultimately arrive at a position in which the relations of "one after the other" would become relations of "one alongside the other." Evidently, that is an impossibility.

Fortunately, something else can be done. At first, we wanted to make

---

[133] Fokker, *art. cit.,* pp. 134-136.

the horizontal lines turn on the same angle as the vertical lines.   In our improper plane, which represents an "enduring straight line," it is better to let the horizontal lines turn in the opposite direction on the same angle as the vertical time tracks.   In this way we get, instead of the squares of the first descriptive frame, rhombuses in the second frame (see Figure Four).   The diagonals, which in a rhombus are always perpendicular to

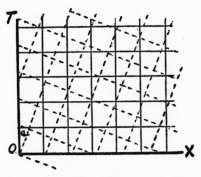

Figure Three

each other, have in this space always the same invariable direction, just as the diagonals of squares.   This point is very important.   For, the invariant character of the direction of the diagonals in any redivision of the XT-diagram indicates that there exists a very special velocity which remains invariant, no matter what division is made.   At the very beginning of his theory Einstein identified this *absolute* velocity with that of light.

It is to be noted also that the area of the rhombus always remains equal to the area of the original congruent squares of the first

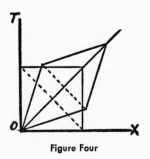

Figure Four

descriptive frame. Now if we draw different rhombuses for different values of the velocity parameter *a,* it follows that the products of the diagonals of these rhombuses always remains constant and equal to the area of the original squares. Conceiving the asymptotes as Cartesian axes, we may therefore say that two angles of the rhombuses drawn from the origin *O* will indicate two hyperbolas. This is wholly in agreement with the fact that an invariant absolute relation is represented by the equation:

$$ds^2 = dt^2 - dx^2 \qquad (7)$$

For, if the velocity parameter *a* passes through all possible values, then formula (7) represents the equation of an hyperbola. If ds^2 is positive, then the hyperbola has its branches upwards and downwards, but if ds^2 is negative, then the hyperbola will have its branches to the left and the right (see Figure Five).

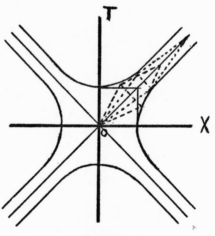

Figure Five

Summarizing, we may say that our "enduring straight line" contains time tracks, i.e., motions composed of temporal durations. It contains also series of events alongside one another represented by lines, which are composed of distances. Finally, the "enduring straight line" contains here-now radii, which are represented as oblique lines with angles of 45 degrees. In this plane we find a square and a series of rhombuses, all of which have equal areas and lie with one vertex in the origin O while another angle slides along a here-now radius in such a way that the other two angles lie on two branches of determined hyperbolas. Since we are dealing here with an improper plane, the rhombuses, despite the contrary suggestion of the drawing, have sides that are absolutely the same size as the square. Two opposite sides of a rhombus represent intervals for the temporal durations, while the other two sides represent distances in the spatial sense.

Three point-events in the "enduring straight line" determine an improper triangle. Several possibilities occur here. The three sides may be temporal durations; they are then motions which meet two by two. In this case, there are two temporal durations, e.g., AB and BC, of which one is wholly before or after the other; for instance, AB before BC. The third side, AC, then contains the point-events lying alongside the point-events of the other two temporal durations (see Figure Six).

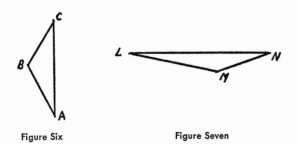

Figure Six   Figure Seven

The three sides can represent also three distances. In that case there are two sides, LM and MN, containing no pair of point-events that lie either before or after each other. All point-events, however, on the third side, NL, are either before or after some of the point-events of the other sides (see Figure Seven).

The three intervals can also consist of two temporal durations and one distance (see Figures Eight, A and B). In that case these temporal durations represent two motions which bridge an initial distance and subsequently meet each other. Or they represent two motions which, after an initial meeting deviate from each other over a certain distance. It is also possible, of course, that the three intervals represent one temporal duration and two distances (see Figure Eight C).

If such triangles contain three sides *of the same kind,* then we find the remarkable property that one side is longer than the other two, which is the opposite of what happens in ordinary Euclidean geometry. Let us assume, then, that ABC is a triangle of temporal durations (see Figure Nine). The temporal duration CB, in that case, can be transferred by an hyperbola to CB'. In the same way AB can be transferred to AB''. From the drawing itself it is clear that $AC > CB' + AB''$, but a

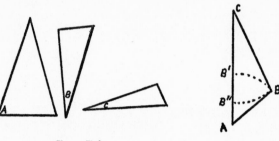

Figure Eight   Figure Nine

simple calculation would lead to the same result. From this theorem it follows at once that the "straight line" is not the shortest line connecting the two events but the *longest*.[134]

Other theorems could be added to complement the theory. We will omit them here and trust that what has been said suffices to illustrate absolute relations and the nature of chronogeometry.[135]

---

[134] Eddington, *Space, Time and Gravitation*, pp. 70-71.

[135] Cf., e.g., Fokker, *art. cit.* Some of the ideas mentioned here are based on oral communications of Professor Fokker. For the examples see also Eddington, *op. cit.*, pp. 45-62.

CHAPTER NINE

"NATURE" AS THE INTENTIONAL CORRELATE OF PHYSICAL SCIENCE, VIEWED FROM THE THEORY OF RELATIVITY

1. The Intentional Correlate of Physical Science

In Chapters Five to Eight we have considered the foundations of the theory of relativity. We must now ask ourselves what the intentional correlate is of the physical attitude proper to this particular physical theory. For, this theory is a well-ordered system of physical statements which, separately and together, intend to say "something" about "something." They express what is in the consciousness of the physicist when he occupies himself with those considerations. Now, as we have seen above, all consciousness is consciousness-of-something.

The Abstract Character of Physical Science. The reply to that question may seem to be obvious. In all his theories and considerations, including the theory of relativity, the physicist speaks, of course, about nature. If this reply were adequate, our question would indeed be very trivial. Yet that question is not a meaningless question, for the point at issue is precisely to determine what exactly is meant here by the term "nature" and how nature, as determined in that way, presents itself in the theory of relativity. What is nature as the intentional correlate of physical science?

One would perhaps be inclined to reply that this nature is the spatio-temporal world, the totality of all spatio-temporal realities. But even this answer is not adequate, for not all aspects which we consider ourselves truthfully bound to ascribe to those realities appear to belong to the essence of the natural object that is the correlate of contemporary physical science.[136] If we compare nature as the object of physical science with nature as we encounter it in our spontaneous, prescientific

---

[136] Husserl, *Ideen,* vol. 2, pp. 1-2.

experience or also with nature as the object of philosophical study or even with nature as the object of all kinds of other attitudes toward the world, it becomes evident that physical science of the things of nature excludes, for example, the aspects of value, beauty, lovableness, perfection, goodness, and usefulness. Ideas such as right, religion, morality, and the state, also are absent from its description of nature. One could reply, of course, that those predicates do not express real properties of nature and that those ideas are meaningless to express reality. However, as we have seen, that kind of scientism is untenable.

True, no objectivities to the constitution of which value judgments or practical acts make an essential contribution play a role in physical science. But the explanation of this situation does not lie in the fact that these objectivities possess "no value for reality," but rather in the typical attitude of the physicist toward the world. For, this attitude is above all a theoretical attitude. Physical science does not arbitrarily "abstract" from the aspects pertaining to the domain of values or the sphere of the practical, but this abstraction is a necessary consequence of the physicist's resolve to assume a purely theoretical attitude toward the world.

A similar explanation should be given for the fact that the so-called "secondary qualities" do not directly occur in the physicist's considerations. For he wants not merely to look at things theoretically, but in the original contact which, as a physicist, he has with the world, he wants to pay attention only to that which he can experience by measuring. By virtue of this attitude, the physicist has *a priori* a certain view of the world, i.e., he constitutes and objectivizes nature in a special way, so that only spatio-temporal objects can continue to appear in the domain of physical science. As Husserl expresses it, "in this 'pure' or purified theoretical attitude we no longer experience houses, tables, streets, works of art; we experience merely material things and of those value-bearing objects we experience only the layer of spatio-temporal materiality."[137]

Physical Science and the Reality of the World. By saying that the proper intentional correlate of physical science is an object constituted by objectivation, we do not intend to assert that physical science does not aim at "real" nature and cannot teach us anything about the "real" world. For, man and the world together constitute worldly be-ings as objects of physical science. The physicist is neither purely passive in the constitution of physical be-ings nor purely active. Man gives meaning,

---

[137] Husserl, *ibid.*, p. 25. See also pp. 24-25 and 4-5.

but it is nature which invites him to give meaning to the world in the physicist's way. The physicist asks questions, but it is nature which invites him to ask questions and which, in its replies, stimulates him to ask further questions. In this way the physicist knows that in his entire science he is in real contact with the real world. Despite the fact, therefore, that the theory is immediately concerned with objective be-ings, it tells us something about the be-ings of reality, not as they are "in themselves," but as we encounter them in our original experience.

These few remarks should suffice for the present. In Part Three we intend to return more in detail to the intentional correlate of physical science in general.

2. The Intentional Correlate of the Physical Attitude in the Theory of Relativity

If the question is asked what the intentional correlate of physical science is in the theory of relativity, several replies are possible. One can say that this correlate is formed by the real world or rather by the totality of real world-events, but one could also reply that the theory wishes to speak about absolute relations between point-events or about space-time. How ambiguous those replies are becomes immediately evident when one attempts to combine them. For, the real world would then have to be equal to space-time, and the totality of real world-events to a well-ordered sum of point-events; hence whatever prescientific experience tells us could not be real unless it could be expressed in the form of absolute relations.

Physical Point-Events and Space-Time. Before delving more deeply into these questions, let us first see what exactly is meant by physical point-events and space-time. By space-time, as we have seen, contemporary physics means the totality of all point-events.[138] At first sight, this description may seem to be very clear. Nevertheless, it is deceptive, for it suggests that the space-time of which the physicist speaks is "that which is present in space and time," since one cannot imagine point-events other than in space and time. No attention is paid here to the fact that the physicist's point-event is, at first, no more than a purely mathematical schematization of a real event of a material particle, which, together with all other particles, forms "that which is present in

---

[138] Synge, *op. cit.,* p. 5.

space and time." The following considerations may serve to clarify the point.

According to Einstein, classical physics viewed space and time as separate physical entities, and temporal determinations did not depend on the choice of frame of reference. The classical physicist spoke, moreover, of points of space and moments of time as if they were absolute realities. He did not realize that the event specified by the four numbers x_1, x_2, x_3, t was the true element of the space-time description. True, an event was always considered a four-dimensional continuum, but the absolute character attributed to time concealed the true meaning of this continuum. Once, however, the absolute character of time and simultaneity had been abandoned, the four-dimensionality of the time-space concept was recognized. Neither the point in space nor the moment of time is meaningful but only the event.[139]

From this one can draw the following conclusion: just as the point in classical physics was no more than the ultimate element of the spatial frame of reference,[140] so the point-event in the theory of relativity is nothing other than the ultimate element of the spatio-temporal frame of reference. Thus space-time, as the sum of all point-events, appears at first only as the spatio-temporal frame of reference itself.[141] In his special theory of relativity Einstein originally conceived space-time, the frame of reference, as a *physical* reality destined to replace Lorentz three-dimensional ether or Newton's absolute space. In the general theory, however, he came to the conclusion that space-time "has no separate existence. . . . Space-time does not claim existence on its own."[142] Space-time, then, is the sum of the mathematical schematizations of *physical* entities.

Physical Reality and Space-Time. E. Beth explains this idea as follows. Empirical statements can be conceived as assertions concerning entities (events) which in physical science can be schematized and arranged in a four-dimensional continuum. When we speak of "physical reality," we refer to the system of events arranged in this fashion, and the continuum used to make this arrangement is called the "physical space-time continuum."[143] This space-time continuum consists of point-

[139] Einstein, *The Meaning of Relativity*, pp. 28-29.

[140] Einstein, *ibid.*, pp. 2-4.

[141] Mund, "Le langage de la physique," L. de Raeymaeker and Others, *La relativité de notre connaissance*, p. 45.

[142] Einstein, *Relativity* . . . , pp. 154-155.

[143] Beth, *Natuurfilosofie*, p. 155.

events as its ultimate constituent elements. When the matter is viewed in this way, a distinction has to be made between:

1. the real *physical* events;

2. the point-events as mathematical schematizations of these events, which by virtue of this schematization imply neither place nor duration and consequently are conceived as spatio-temporally unextended;[144]

3. space-time as the sum of all point-events or the spatio-temporal frame of description.

Accordingly, the question concerning the intentional correlate of the theory of relativity amounts to asking what we mean when in this connection we speak of "real physical events." As should be evident from the preceding considerations, this term does not refer to the events of reality *as* we experience them in our prescientific life but to those same events *solely* insofar as they have measurable aspects. Taken as such, therefore, those "real physical events" are objectivized entities.

The Dynamic Reality of Physical Events. The obvious question to arise here is, of course, what exactly is the connection between the physical events and the events which we encounter in our original experiences? It appears to us that the theory of relativity wants to emphasize the fact that the world view of classical physics was too static because its abstraction and schematization went too far. On the basis of a spontaneous "natural" experience, it conceived the world in a three-dimensional fashion. It did not seem to realize that it reduced reality to an almost meaningless abstraction, for, by depriving it of one dimension, classical physics reduced a dynamic reality to a static one, without having any real justification for its procedure.

In connection with this matter the theory of relativity asserts that between two point-events of different moving material particles there exists a primary relation, viz., a spatio-temporal relation, and that this relation possesses an objective and absolute character, contrary to the case of the exclusively spatial or the exclusively temporal relations between these two particles. The exclusively spatial or exclusively temporal relations are based on an abstraction that goes too far and therefore are neither objective nor absolute, but dependent on the chosen frame of reference. Between two point-events of one and the same particle an exclusively temporal relation is *per se* possible: for particles moving with the velocity of light, whose world lines, therefore, coincide

---

[144] Synge, *op. cit.*, p. 5.

in a graphical representation with those of a beam of light, the magnitude of this relation is zero.[145]   Finally, the totality of all point-events is called "space-time" in the theory of relativity.

On the basis of these statements, contemporary physical science considers speaking about a physical space as independent of a physical time also as an abstraction that goes too far and to which nothing corresponds immediately in the physical world.   Let us mention, however, that most physicists insist on adding explicitly that this statement does not at all intend to take away or minimize the fundamental distinction between the dimensions of space and that of time.[146]

The Essential Temporality of Nature.   Be all this as it may, it appears to be the fundamental intention of the theory of relativity to emphasize most strongly that physical entities are not static but dynamic realities.   If that is true, then it is no longer difficult to determine the bond of those physical events with reality, as we encounter it in our original experience.   The question concerning this bond may perhaps be proposed in another, more suitable form: What does the theory of relativity ultimately tell us about reality as such?   In the reply to this question it must be kept in mind that the statements of the theory itself are immediately concerned with physical quantities and physical entities. Moving material particles, absolute spatio-temporal relations, etc., are nothing other than physical realities, i.e., objects which are constituted solely in and by physical science.   But these objects are constituted in a living dialogue of the physicist with the world, and in this dialogue there are of necessity both elements coming from the side of the physicist and elements coming from the side of nature.   The physicist projects a certain view of nature and builds on this view in the development of his theories.   That which is irrelevant in real be-ings with respect to his attitude is discarded, and that which is relevant in his vision is considered only insofar as it fits into the frame of the physicist's project.   Nature, on the other hand, also makes its demands, and the physicist's questions have to take those demands into account if he does not want to cut short his real dialogue with the real world.

If, then, the theory of relativity can show that contact with the real world is broken when one attempts to force the world into a three-dimensional view, while the dialogue can be continued when nature is

---

[145] Synge, *ibid.,* pp. 32-34.
[146] Einstein, *The Meaning of Relativity,* pp. 28-29.

viewed in a four-dimensional frame, then it follows that nature is intrinsically and essentially temporal. This conclusion is confirmed by the fact that between point-events of one and the same material particle there can be an exclusively temporal relation, but not an exclusively spatial relation. By saying that natural be-ings are essentially temporal, we express nothing else but the fact that the being of worldly be-ings is a coming-to-be.

3. Being and Becoming

The intentional correlate, then, of the theory of relativity is formed by the events occurring in reality but viewed solely in their measurable aspects. Nevertheless, the theory continues to aim, through those objectivized entities, at the real events which we experience in our original contact with the world. Concerning these events, the theory of relativity throws a mediate but very strong light on the fact that their being has to be a coming-to-be.

The statement that natural "being" and "becoming" are identical brings us back to a venerable old, but often forgotten, view. According to E. Hardy, the Greek term *physis* (nature) was originally a collective term indicating in general the world of observable phenomena.[147] The term soon received a second derivative sense: alongside the world of observable phenomena, it came to be used also to indicate the substratum lying at the root of those phenomena. Connected with this second meaning was the fact that as early as the time of Thales the idea "change" began to occupy a very prominent, and even the first, place with respect to the idea of being, so that for Thales and his contemporaries being became identical with coming-to-be.[148] As A. Mansion expresses it, "Let us repeat that for the thinkers before Socrates cosmic *physis* encompassed the whole of natural phenomena occurring in the world, together with the primitive material reality which is their source and origin. In a more restricted sense, which is closer to its etymological meaning, the term *physis* also indicated simply material coming-to-be. This idea of coming-to-be, moreover, was never entirely absent from the meaning of the term."[149] For Plato and Aristotle also the fundamental

---

[147] E. Hardy, *Der Begriff der Physis in der Griechischen Philosophie,* Berlin, 1884, pp. 13-35.

[148] A. Mansion, *Introduction à la physique aristotélicienne,* pp. 59-63.

[149] Mansion, *ibid.,* p. 63.

problem of the philosophy of nature remained the "explanation of cosmic coming-to-be,"[150] so that here again we find implied the identity of being and coming-to-be for things of nature.

Starting from entirely different ideas, Heidegger arrives at a similar conclusion. He writes: "In the age of the earliest and crucial unfolding of Western philosophy among the Greeks, who first raised the authentic question of be-ing as such in its entirety, be-ing was called *physis*. . . . What does the word *physis* denote? It denotes self-blossoming emergence, . . . the realm of things that emerge and linger on. . . . This power of emerging and enduring includes 'becoming' as well as 'being' in the restricted sense of inert duration. *Physis* is the process of a-rising."[151] Unlike Heidegger, however, we think that *physis* in the original sense indicated, for both the Pre-Socratics and Aristotle, only the world of observable phenomena, so that in Greek philosophy only for things of nature are being and coming-to-be identical or at least necessarily imply each other.[152] However, we do not want to enter into this problem here, for its thematic study pertains to the philosophy of inorganic nature.

---

[150] Mansion, *ibid.,* p. 65.

[151] Heidegger, *Introduction to Metaphysics,* New York, 1961, pp. 11-13.

[152] It may be important to point out in this connection that the Latin term *existere* in its classical period did not have a static but a dynamic meaning. Cf. C. Verhoeven, "De betekenis van het woord 'existere,' " *Studia catholica,* vol. 32, pp. 1-28.

PART THREE
PHYSICAL SCIENCE: ITS NATURE AND RELATION TO PHILOSOPHY

Introductory Remarks

We have finally reached the stage where it becomes possible to describe the proper meaning of man's activity in the pursuit of contemporary physical science. During the first few centuries the physical sciences went through a period of fairly gradual development. Since the end of the past century this development appears to assume an ever-increasing speed. We note, moreover, that since 1900 there have been rather profound changes on many points regarding the question of what physical science really is. Certain fundamental views of classical physics have been subjected to a critical analysis and replaced by theories of contemporary physics, such as the theories of relativity and quantum mechanics.

On closer inspection, this change of standpoint does not appear to be concerned primarily with the fundamental principles proper to the aim of physical science as such. It aims, on the contrary, at the assumed fundamental convictions which *de facto* revealed themselves based on *a priori* positions foreign to physical science itself and mostly of a philosophical origin. The truth of this assertion is manifest, e.g., from the fact that, despite all changes, the major chapters of classical physics can be viewed as being concerned with boundary cases of the most important contemporary theories and as retaining their importance for certain more closely defined areas. Accordingly, no matter how profoundly and manifestly contemporary physics differs from classical physics, physical science today still possesses essentially the same inner structure and expansive force as it had in the seventeenth century.

Be this as it may, in any case the question about the proper meaning of man's activity in the pursuit of physical science may today be raised on a new level. For, in its present phase of development physical science presents itself in a much purer form because it contains less speculative considerations that are foreign to physical science. It is easier now to look at the rigorously scientific activity of the physicist, without having to take into account philosophical implications that could be implied in the scientifically acquired data. It is true, of course, that even now all kinds of epistemological and ontological considerations are connected with the theories of contemporary physics. The writings of such prominent physicists as Einstein, Planck, Bohr, de Broglie, Heisenberg, Schrödinger, and Dirac contain many examples of such considerations. However, those speculations do not flow of necessity from the essence itself of physical science. And, what is more important, they do not constitute a part of the physical train of thought. In the technical literature of physical science itself such speculations are but rarely present; so that, generally speaking, it is not too difficult to distinguish the philosophical consideration from the strictly physical train of thought. Consequently, it will not be too arduous a task to apply a reduction to those philosophical implications and interpretations, to describe and analyze the purely scientific pursuit of the physicist as such, in order to inquire into its meaning and to make an attempt to solve that question.[1]

When we inquire into the proper meaning of the physicist's scientific activity, several problems connected with this question rise almost at the same time. What exactly is the intentional correlate of physical science? What is this correlate's status of being? What is the method of physical science? How are we to explain the function which mathematics fulfills in physics? What kind of a bond is there between "abstract" mathematics and "concrete" physical science? What is the function and meaning of experiments, laws, and theories? How are we to explain the typical conceptual structure of physical science? What exactly is physical science's own view concerning truth and certainty? What makes man pursue physical science? What is his principal motive? Is it the usefulness of this science for man's welfare, in technology, in the desire to have practical control of the world or rather in the desire to know and understand? What is the connection between the world of physical science and the world of our ordinary, spontaneous experience? What exactly is the relationship between physical science and philosophy?

In the following pages we will attempt to find a reply to the most important of these questions. Our starting point will consist of the phenomenological theory of science described in Part One and of the data which in the analysis of Part Two we have discovered concerning contemporary physical science and its intentional correlate. Our reply will be hardly more than a first attempt, a first step in, we hope, the right direction.

---

[1] H. van de Hulst and C. van Peursen, *Phaenomenologie en natuurwetenschap,* Utrecht, 1953, pp. 78-87.

CHAPTER TEN

THE PROPER CHARACTER
OF PHYSICAL SCIENCE

1. The World of the Physicist

Our attempt to give an accurate description of the character proper to contemporary physical science may, perhaps, best begin with the fact that modern physics itself now realizes that it does not mirror an objectively pre-given world, because the proper object of the physical sciences cannot be divorced from the physicist's approach to nature. While it is true that the train of physical thought goes on in man after he has made contact with the world in a particular way and that nature itself clearly offers man an opportunity to pursue that kind of knowledge, nonetheless that knowledge cannot be called a mirroring of a pre-given rationality. Against the positivistic interpretation of the erroneous prejudice claiming such a rationality, one can argue that the laws of nature discovered by "induction" cannot mirror a pre-given order of nature, since that order exists only for and through the physicist. And, on the other hand, against the rationalistic interpretation one can point out that the physicist does not constitute that order all by himself, because he clearly constructs his field of meaning in a constant contact with the world.

The Physicist's Presence in the World. The phenomenological theory of science appears to offer a suitable way to develop this fundamental idea and to describe the world of physics more accurately. It rejects the two absolute poles, proclaimed by the above-mentioned prejudice, of a world-without-man and a man-without-a-world. Our thinking can never be concerned with a world that is wholly independent of man, but, on the other hand, the process of our thinking does not remain contained within its own interiority. Man, including the physicist, is whatever he is, in the world. Reversely, the world, including the world of physical science, is permeated with man's presence. This presence of man in the world is never wholly passive; it is always a giving of meaning; it always demarcates a certain field of

163

presence. On the other hand, neither is it wholly active, for nature imposes itself on man and always makes certain demands.

The physicist, therefore, knows that in his science he is in real contact with the real world. The world invites him to assume a determined attitude toward itself. The physicist accepts this invitation and begins by asking questions. He selects his questions in such a way that nature is forced to reply in a determined way. These replies invite him to ask further questions, destined to lead to well-defined replies because they force nature to reply in such a fashion. In this way a certain field of meaning develops, and within this field the world of physical science receives its form and structure.[2]

Theory of Reality. As is the case with all other sciences, the physicist assumes a theoretical attitude in his science. He detaches himself from his original intentional orientation to the world, in which he lived originally and in which he was totally involved in the world. He wants only to observe and contemplate. In correspondence with this new attitude toward the world, the original everyday world of life changes for him into an "objective world." Nevertheless, the essence of modern science may and must be described as a "theory concerning the real," provided the terms "theory" and "reality" are correctly understood.

The term "reality" is used to indicate both that which makes something be by realizing it and that which has been made real in this way and is now present. In both cases it is proper to the real, understood in this sense, that it becomes unconcealed and dwells in the light of this unconcealedness. The typical feature of contemporary science, now, is that it wants to consider this presence of worldly things only as an "objective being-an-object-of." In other words, for those sciences reality is identical with being-an-object-of.

The term "theory," on the other hand, initially put special emphasis on the passive element of gazing at something. In the modern idea of "theory," however, an active element is also implied and even primarily so. He who wants to contemplate something theoretically, must now begin by handling what he will see later; he marks it off and separates the thing he wants to consider as an object by constituting it in its condition of being-an-object-of his consideration.[3]

---

[2] Cf. above, Chapter Seven.
[3] Heidegger, "Wissenschaft und Besinnung," *Vorträge und Aufsätze,* Pfullingen, 1959, pp. 46-59.

Physical Science as Theory of the Objective Dimension of Reality.
For this reason one could perhaps say with de Waelhens that, like every
other positive science, physics is essentially a theory of the objective
dimension of reality, which is primarily and in the full sense of the term
an encounter. For, both science as well as philosophy are a real
unfolding of reality. Their distinction lies in the fact that in their
unfolding they move on different levels and are concerned with different
levels of reality.

This distinction may be clarified by showing, with Husserl, that the
object of philosophy, unlike that of science, presupposes a phenomenological reduction. Science abstracts from the intentional movement which
orientates us to things, i.e., it takes its objects as simply given and does
not know that those objects disclosed themselves originally within an
encounter and a co-existence. Phenomenological philosophy, on the
other hand, wants to describe precisely the innumerable modalities of
that encounter and co-existence in their noematic and noetic aspects.
But if reality is ultimately the co-existence of myself and the world, the
orientation of the world to me and my openness to the world, in which
meaning originally constitutes itself in numberless modalities, then it
follows that science, as a real unfolding of reality within the sphere of
the natural attitude, is nothing other than a theory of the objective side
of reality. For, within perceptive co-existence itself one can, abstractly
speaking, discern a purely objective side, viz., the domain of the other
than the perceiver. For this reason it is a constitutive element of all
positive sciences that they simply have to consider that which they study
as given. What physical science studies is not "the fullness of reality"
but something "abstract," something "objective," which as such does not
exist, but which physical science in its original physical project of the
world constitutes and which as such, therefore, does not escape from the
sphere of intentionality.[4]

Theory and Praxis. As we have seen above, in his science the
physicist assumes a theoretical attitude; he detaches himself from the
original intentional orientation to the world which involves him fully in
this world. He merely wants to observe and contemplate the world and
its things. In correspondence with this new attitude, the original world
of life becomes an "objective" world: that which in the original

---

[4] de Waelhens, "Science, phénoménologie, ontologie," *Existence et signification,* Louvain, 1958, pp. 107-109.

intentionality appeared as "ready-to-hand" (*Zuhandenes*) for his daily "concern" (*Besorgen*) remains only as "present-at-hand" (*vorhanden*). In connection with this point, one could ask how the practical manipulating is changed into purely theoretical contemplation. At first sight, one would perhaps be inclined to say that this change is brought about merely because the person in question abstains from all *praxis*. In other words, the essential element in the origin of the theoretical attitude would be the disappearance of the *praxis*. If, then, one regards practical concern as the primary and dominating mode of being of man in his concrete life, "theory" seems to owe its ontological possibility to a privation, i.e., when *praxis* is dropped, only theory remains.

It is hardly necessary to point out that this view is erroneous. For, any *praxis* needs such a theoretical gazing from time to time, and on the other hand, in many cases theory cannot exist without *praxis*. One has merely to think in this connection of the technical skill that is implied in the use of the complex measuring instruments needed in contemporary physical science. Moreover, even man's practical handling of things implies a kind of "circumspection," an insight and survey which will ultimately assume the form of a deliberating study. It is precisely this "vision" of things as "ready-to-hand" that has to be changed if the theoretical attitude is to arise. The theoretical attitude, therefore, does not consist of discarding the *praxis,* but in the fact that one looks in a new way at that which is "ready-to-hand" of our daily care, conceiving and projecting it as "present-at-hand."

Accordingly, the physical world view is the consequence of a change in man's attitude to the world, a change which fundamentally modifies the primarily given world view. The result of this change is that the things which man at first, within the framework of his original world, "manipulated" now receive a new character; they are detached from their original world (*Entweltlichung*) and appear now only in a frame that is no longer brought into relation with man and stripped of all limits (*entschränkt*). The root of this new attitude toward the world lies in what Heidegger calls "thematization."[5]

The Physicist's Thematization and Field of Meaning. The theoretical gaze, then, is rooted in a thematization. But that thematization allows the theoretical man many possibilities. Which aspect of the

---

[5] Heidegger, *Sein und Zeit,* pp. 59-62, 153-160, 356-364 (English ed., pp. 86-90, 195-203, 408-415) ; de Waelhens, *La philosophie de Martin Heidegger,* Louvain, 1955, pp. 40-49, 87-98, 197-205; van de Hulst and van Peursen, *op. cit.,* pp. 38-42.

worldly be-ings will be considered depends on the proper character of the thematizing project. The physicist, as we have seen, wants to question the world only through measurement. By this decision he thematizes the worldly be-ings as required by his resolve, and at the same time he makes them his object in such a way that henceforth he can question them only in this fashion.[6]

At the same time, by virtue of this new attitude of wanting to question nature only through measurement, the physicist also projects a certain field of meaning, within which only be-ings of a certain "kind" have any relevance. This field is the domain of the measurable, of what somehow is extended. Being-measurable, therefore, is the formality under which in this case all be-ings of this domain will be considered; being-measurable is the formal aspect of all worldly be-ings insofar as they are the object of the physical attitude toward the world. But this measurability and extension are not objective properties of objective things that exist independently of man in a world-in-itself. They are only invitations addressed to us, modalities in which be-ings let themselves be encountered by man.

Thus, the whole of whatever is immediately or mediately measurable constitutes for the physicist the "region" of the physical. If he rigorously adheres to the necessary demand to consider any worldly event only in the light of this fundamental attitude, then his train of thought will possess a rigorous form and attain to the exactness that is characteristic of physical science.[7]

Original Project and Method of Research. The original project determines also the direction which the investigation will have to take from the viewpoint of method. For, if the entire "region" has to become objective, then the physicist must try to "encounter" this domain in all its layers and branches. But the domain of worldly be-ings is constantly changing and developing. For this reason physical science must pay attention to this changeability in all its activities. It is only against this horizon of unending change that the facts manifest themselves fully. But these facts have to be made "objective." Hence in his pursuit of science the physicist will have to represent the changeable in its changes;

---

[6] Heidegger, *op. cit.*, pp. 362-363 (English ed., pp. 413-415).

[7] Heidegger, "Die Zeit des Weltbildes," *Holzwege*, Frankfurt a.M., 1957, pp. 71-73. Concerning the meaning of the term "region" see Husserl, *Ideen*, vol. 1, pp. 13, 23-29, 37-39; vol. 3, pp. 1-21, 25-37; Gurwitsch, *The Field of Consciousness*, pp. 189-190.

he has to bring this change to a standstill and nonetheless allow it to go on.

One could speak of the identity of the facts in the continuance of their changes as "regularity" and speak of the continuance of the change with its character of necessity as law. In other words, only in the light of regularity and laws do the facts become intelligible. The investigation of facts, therefore, always implies that rules and laws are formulated and verified. This formulation, however, in its turn, always implies two aspects: on the one hand, the unknown is explained by means of the known, i.e., the laws established by the physicist; but on the other, these laws and rules are ultimately to be verified in experiments by the facts themselves. Laws and experiments, however, do not yet imply understanding. This phase is reached only when, after comparison, the connection between the various experimental facts and laws becomes clear. Since in physical science facts are allowed to speak only by way of measuring instruments, physical laws essentially provide us with relations between numbers discovered through measurement. Hence it is mathematics which, on the basis of the initial attitude of physics toward worldly be-ings, opens us the approach to the correct understanding of the object constituted by that approach.

Mathematics, therefore, is an essential part of the physical theory. But, if mathematics is to remain a part of a physical theory, the mathematical argument has to proceed from the basis of experiments and laws and ultimately to terminate in experiments. The experiment, therefore, is also an essential factor of the process of physical thought and it, too, imposes its well-defined methodic demands. Nevertheless, these dual demands do not make physical science ambiguous from the methodic viewpoint. For the intrinsic finality of every physical experiment demands that it lead us to metric numbers between which natural laws can establish relationships. The mathematical treatment in a certain sense starts with the result thus obtained and, on the other hand, also terminates ultimately in experiments. In other words, the measuring experiments, which through their numbers and laws supply us with the starting point for the mathematical treatment, constitute the necessary link between the physical theories, which are largely mathematical, and the world-of-nature about which the physicist really wants to speak.[8]

---

[8] Heidegger, *art. cit.* in footnote 7, pp. 71-76.

Summarizing, therefore, we can say that man in questioning nature always assumes a very definite attitude. This attitude is quite different from the one he has in ordinary life when his whole being is involved. For, in the original contact between man and the world nature imposes itself on man as something extended. This being-extended with its various modalities invites man to make comparisons, and this comparing becomes at once measuring as soon as man connects it with fixed, though freely chosen, norms and measures. Measuring, which is merely a form of questioning the world, provides us with numbers inviting us to further comparisons. And in this way we are led to formulate laws as mathematical relationships between metric numbers.

Next, the plurality of laws invites us to arrange them in orderly fashion through mathematics. This gives rise to the mathematical theories whose mathematically deductive system has to be interpreted, with or without the aid of models, in such a way that its validity with respect to the actual events of nature can be verified through suitable experiments. But in the entire process it is man who, questioningly, seeks and establishes connections wherever questioned nature forces him to dis-cover such connections. Metric numbers, laws, and theories, therefore, do not describe "objectively" the "objective" properties of a world-in-itself, but arise only in and through the intentional relationship of the physicist to the world. For this reason they are valid only within the field of meaning proper to this mode of intentionality.[9]

Finally, it should be evident that this proper method imposes on the physicist the use of a special terminology and a special symbolism. Ultimately, however, all this is already implied in the original thematic project of the physicist.[10]

The Physicist's View of Truth and Certainty. The physicist's view of truth and certainty also is fundamentally determined by his original thematic project. For phenomenology, the truth of physics does not lie in the internal coherence of a complex of concepts and ideas nor in a faithful mirroring of a pre-given order of facts pertaining to a world-in-itself. Nor can this truth consist in an agreement of knowledge and being, at least not if being is conceived as independent of man. But a physical statement is true if it is concerned with nature in the way nature should be addressed within the mode of intentionality proper to the physicist. As long as nature continues to give meaningful replies to the

---

[9] Heidegger, *art. cit.* in footnote 3, pp. 55-56, 59-63.
[10] Heidegger, *Sein und Zeit,* pp. 362-363 (English ed., pp. 413-415).

questions which the physicist asks, the questions and the statements of the physicist are true; hence a physical statement is true as long as experiments confirm what the physicist suspects on the basis of his theories. To demand more than that is to surrender to an illusion. Each subsequent experiment may confirm this truth, but it can also apodictically show that nature is "unfamiliar" with our question, that we question it in a way which does not "suit" it.

One could insist, of course, and ask: What does that physical truth consist of when the experiments confirm our expectations? The reply is: truth consists in the fact that, within this mode of thematization, we address ourselves to nature in a way which reveals itself in harmony with its compelling character. It would be meaningless to propose any other kind of reply.

For phenomenology, moreover, the compelling character of the answer nature gives to the physicist's question is one of the principal reasons for the certainty and typical exactness of the physical sciences. In other respects this exactness appears to be the necessary consequence of the radical abstraction and schematization of physical science, for in this way it is possible to use mathematics, the exact science *par excellence,* as our method in the study of the objects constituted by the physical thematization. All this presupposes, of course, that the physicist in his entire procedure remains within the field of meaning constituted in and through his original thematizing project.[11]

2. *Physical Science and Technology*

Intimate Bond Between Science and Technology. The modern world is a convincing demonstration of the bond existing between physical science and technology. Furthermore, the history of both shows clearly that their development has always been parallel. Technology has spread the physical science of the West over the entire world and at the same time has secured for it a central place in the pre-occupations of today's thinkers. In the development of the past two hundred years, technology has constantly manifested itself as both a presupposition and a consequence of physical science. It is a presupposition insofar as the expansion and penetration of physical science often depend on the technical

---

[11] Heidegger, *art. cit.* in footnote 7, pp. 79-80, 72-73; R. Kwant and J. van den Berk, "Het gesprek van de physicus met de wereld,"[0] *Annalen v.h. Thijmgenootschap,* vol. 43, pp. 12-15.

refinement of the means of observation. It is a consequence insofar as the technical utilization of natural forces is, generally speaking, possible only on the basis of a profound study of the relevant domain of experience.

The bond between physical science and technology becomes even more manifest when one investigates more concretely in history how these two have always determined and complemented each other. The technique of the eighteenth and nineteenth centuries, for example, had to rely on the use of purely mechanical procedures, which ultimately reached their apex in the steam engine. The machines of that era did what man formerly had to do himself and often even imitated man's way of handling tools. This form of technique was viewed therefore as a continuation and renewal of the old manual techniques. As soon, however, as electrotechnical processes began to develop, technology assumed a different character. There was hardly any question of a bond between technique and manual crafts. It now became much more a utilization of natural forces that were largely unknown to man in his everyday life. Even today electrotechnical processes seem strange and somewhat frightening to many who, even if they know how to use them in practice, still find them incomprehensible.

Chemical technique at first appeared to be closely allied to certain old types of crafts, but modern chemical processes are again beyond comparison with familiar procedures of daily life. Finally, in atomic technology there is question only of utilizing natural forces which are not even accessible to us from the world of ordinary experience. It is possible, of course, that we will become as familiar with this kind of technology as we are with electro-technology, but it will never become a part of nature in the original sense of the term.[12]

The assertion that there exist an undeniable bond between physical science and technology does not tell us anything yet about the root of their interconnection. For, one could claim either that technology is applied physical science or also that technology is the ultimate root of the physicist's theoretical study. Which of these two replies is correct will have to be determined by a study of the essence of technology. While we are unable to develop this point here extensively, it may be useful to attempt briefly to indicate the standpoint of phenomenology in this matter.

Technology and Unconcealedness. The question of what the essence

---

[12] Heisenberg, *Das Naturbild der heutigen Physik,* Hamburg, 1957, pp. 12-15.

of technology is will be a great mystery as long as one does not go beyond the technical phenomenon as a fact.[13]   For asking what the essence of technology is, is asking what, *properly speaking,* technology is.   This question is usually answered by saying that it is a means to attain certain goals.   Others try to define technology as a special way of man's acting. Both of these aspects, obviously, are involved, for only man can set himself a purpose or goal.   This approach to the question could be called the instrumental or anthropological description of technology.   It is hardly necessary to add that such a characterization of technology is correct and applies not only to ancient forms of technical handling but also to contemporary technological procedures.

The question, however, is whether such a reply indicates the essence of technology.   For, a correct reply is not at all always identical with a true reply in the philosophical sense of the term.   On the other hand, it is possible that the instrumental description of technology may lead to a definition of its essence.   The first step in this direction should be a reflection on the proper meaning of instrumental causality.[14]

The famous doctrine of the four causes is, as everyone knows, of Aristotelian origin.   The current interpretation of this doctrine, however, dates from later times and does not always do full justice to what Aristotle originally had in mind.   For, the term *aition* used by Aristotle is usually interpreted as that which gives rise to something else.   In its original sense, however, this term means "to be guilty of," although one should keep in mind that in the present context the expression "to be guilty of" implies nothing ethical or pragmatical.   Through the analysis of simple examples Heidegger shows how the four causes in four different ways "are guilty of" the appearance and the being-in-itself of a utensil.   Despite these differences, the four causes agree in that they make present that which was not yet present, that they make it come forward, draw it from concealedness into unconcealedness.   Viewed in this way, cause is connected with *a-lētheia,* a term that is usually translated as "truth."[15]   For a clearer understanding of the matter, it will be useful to dwell briefly on this view of truth.

According to phenomenology, we must make a distinction between the

---

[13] For what follows cf. Heidegger, "Die Frage nach der Technik," *Vortrage und Aufsätze,* pp. 13-44 (also reprinted in *Die Künste im technischen Zeitalter,* München, 1956, pp. 48-72).

[14] Heidegger, *ibid.,* pp. 13-15.

[15] Heidegger, *ibid.,* pp. 15-20.

truth ascribed to human judgments and a more fundamental sense that can and should be attached to the term "truth." The truth of judgments may be described, with Aristotle and the Scholastics, as the "agreement of the intellect with the thing." But even then one should not lose sight of the idea of intentionality. The "thing" of which there is question here, the reality, is not the thing-in-itself but the thing as it appears to me in my encounter with the world. Alongside this "truth of judgment," there is a more fundamental form of truth which lies not primarily in a judgment but in human existence itself. For the agreement of the judgment with "reality" presupposes that reality has already been drawn from concealedness in a more original way. But to draw reality from concealedness into unconcealedness (*a-lētheia*) requires a certain "light," a *lumen naturale,* to use the historical term. This "light" is conscious existence itself, our conscious being-in-and-to-the-world, from which originally all meaning draws its light.[16]

At first sight, it may seem that there is no clear connection between this idea of truth and the essence of technology. On closer inspection, however, the two are seen to be essentially related. For, *a-lētheia,* as the original bringing to light, is the root of all other bringing to light, of all other dis-coveries and dis-closures, and on the other hand, the common element of the four causes, including the instrumental causality characterizing technology, is precisely that they dis-close and dis-cover.

If these ideas are right, then technology should be conceived as a mode of bringing to light, of dis-covering, so that there exists a close connection between technology and "truth." Technology dis-covers things which cannot dis-close themselves. But, then, the essence of technology does not consist of making or using tools or instruments, but precisely in this typical modality of bringing-to-light. If in the ancient handicrafts this bringing to light was mainly a question of making things effectively, in modern technology the aspect of dis-covery and dis-closure is more predominant. For today's technology forces nature to unlock its energy and to surrender its forces. It harnesses the forces of nature, transforms, accumulates and conserves them; then it divides again what

16 Heidegger, *Vom Wesen der Wahrheit,* Frankfurt a.M., 1954, pp. 9-19 (English ed. "On the Essence of Truth," *Existence and Being,* pp. 321-330); *Sein und Zeit,* pp. 212-230 (English ed., pp. 256-273); de Waelhens, *Phénoménologie et vérité,* Paris, 1953, pp. 63-166 (*passim*); Luijpen, *Existential Phenomenology,* pp. 143-144; Kockelmans, "Het standpunt van de phaenomenologie met betreeking tot de vraag over de verhouding tussen zijn en verschijnen," *Tijdschrift voor Philosophie,* vol. 22, pp. 544-587.

it has conserved and accumulated to transform it again and use it. It is in this way that contemporary technology brings things to light.[17]

The Essence of Technology. What, we may now ask, is the character of the unconcealedness proper to that which is brought to light through contemporary technology? It appears that the typical character of technology's products must be sought in the fact that whatever is brought into being through technology has no other meaning than that of being ever ready to become a part of an effective process. An airplane, for example, stands ready on the apron of the airport to render secure the possibility of transporting men and materials. This typical mode of being of the technical product could be indicated by saying that it is always "in supply," but this expression does not do full justice to it. Heidegger uses here the term *Bestand.* His intention may perhaps be clarified in the following way. From our original being-in-the-world, in which we deal with the worldly be-ings around us through our concern (*Besorgen*), we are able to pass to a different attitude toward these be-ings through a thematizing and objectivizing project, so that henceforth those be-ings can appear to us only as objects. In a similar way we are able, through a different change of attitude, to make the things of our daily concern appear to us henceforth only as *Bestand,* by pro-ducing them in such a way that they are steadily at our disposal. Thus, that which is before us as *Bestand,* as such, can no longer meet us as an object.[18]

It is, of course, man himself who through his attitude toward the be-ings of the world makes worldly things appear as *Bestand.* But because of the essential intentionality existing between man and the world man can do this only insofar as he himself is invited to force nature to surrender its energy. Now, since man is more originally invited by nature itself to make the worldly be-ing appear as *Bestand* than nature's energy is forced by him to be readily at his disposal, man himself can never become *Bestand.* When man pursues technology, he simply pursues one of the many ways in which worldly be-ings can be forced to dis-close themselves.[19]

How exactly does technology dis-close worldly be-ings? Whenever man opens his eyes or ears or does anything at all, as man, about worldly be-ings he consciously is in the unconcealed. When he investigates and

---

[17] Heidegger, *art. cit.* in footnote 15, pp. 20-24.

[18] Heidegger, *ibid.,* pp. 24-25.

[19] Heidegger, *ibid.,* pp. 25-27.

examines nature with a theoretical gaze, then he uses a mode of bringing to light which invites him to encounter the object thus met also in a different fashion. It invites him to make it appear also in the objectless realm of the *Bestand* through technology, so that it will stand unconcealed in a new way. If this view is correct, then we should not view technology as a consequence of physical science, as is suggested by history, but rather physical science in function of the *essence* of technology; although science was first "in execution," technology was first in a, perhaps still unconscious, intention.[20]

This brief consideration does not solve all the questions that can arise here. Nevertheless, we hope that it may serve to indicate the direction in which phenomenology looks for an answer to the question regarding the relationship between science and technology. Or, differently expressed, we hope that it will help us to find a reply to the question about the ultimate motive which drives man to thematize and objectivize nature as he has actually been doing for centuries.

---

[20] Heidegger, *ibid.,* pp. 27-31. Concerning the relationship between science and technology see also van Melsen, *Science and Technology,* Pittsburgh, 1961.

CHAPTER ELEVEN

PHYSICAL SCIENCE AND PHILOSOPHY

1. Collaboration of Science and Philosophy

Distinction but No Opposition. In the preceding pages we have seen that, according to the phenomenological theory of science, there is a real distinction between physical science and philosophy. We have noted also that this distinction does not at all imply rivalry between these two intellectual disciplines or that one makes the other superfluous. Both aim to explain man and the world in which he lives, but the meaning of the term "explanation" is quite different in the two cases because the attitude and standpoint toward the world are divergent. Philosophy views the world precisely insofar as it manifests itself essentially related to man in man's most original experience, which is his existence itself. Physical science, on the other hand, limits itself to study a certain aspect of the world's objective dimension, which for this purpose it first constitutes as an object through its original thematization. Nevertheless, this difference, as well as others connected with it, do not contain anything that should lead to opposition and rivalry. On the contrary, there are reasons urging the necessity of mutual collaboration.[21] The question, now, is how this collaboration should be concretely conceived.

Philosophy Endeavors to Understand the Physical Attitude. The first point to be mentioned here would be the fact that philosophy endeavors to understand the physical attitude as such in order to discover the peculiar structure proper to the physical field of presence. In that attempt philosophy will endeavor to understand how the physical attitude is rooted in our primordial experience and how the field of meaning proper to the physical sciences explicitates and explains the objective dimension of our original field of presence. Its main questions

---

[21] Merleau-Ponty, *Sens et Non-Sens,* pp. 194-195; de Waelhens, *Une philosophie de l'ambiguïté,* p. 391; Kwant, "Het phenomenologisch wetenschapsideaal," *Tijdschrift voor Zielkunde en Opvoedingsleer,* vol. 41, pp. 38-39.

176

in this matter are: What is the meaning of the intentional correlate of the physical sciences? and: Are these sciences knowledge of reality, and if so, in what respect?[22]

In the preceding chapters we have tried to reply to these questions and to see them in the light of the theory of relativity. It seems to us, however, that the reply to those questions is merely a first step. Everything is not said and done when the proper meaning of the physicist's activity and the ontological status of his intentional correlate have been given a foundation and explanation. For, when that task has been executed, one does not yet see how the physical sciences, on their side, can contribute anything to philosophy, as appears to be implied in the assertion that the two disciplines should collaborate. In other words, it will be necessary to enter into greater detail.

No Single All-Encompassing Synthesis. On the other hand, it should be immediately evident that the relationship between physical science and philosophy cannot be such that one either attributes immediately a philosophical content to the statements of physical science or interprets these statements against a particular ontological background. It is simply impossible to unite the data of physics with the results of a philosophical study in a single rational synthesis. It is useless, therefore, to try to verify philosophical categories in the theories and concepts of physics or to look there for such categories.

This point could be explained in the following way. The world of physical thought is a field of encounter constituted by a particular human attitude and therefore permeated with a sphere of thinking entirely its own. One cannot find there the categories pertaining to other possible attitudes, even though the opposite may be suggested by a superficial similarity of terms. The attempt to merge the many worlds of thought proper to the various sciences into a single rational synthesis is inspired by the assumption that all sciences speak about one and the same objective world. But our rejection of this synthesis and our recognition of the fact that there exist as many fields of presence as there are different attitudes toward the world simply leave no room for such an attempt.[23]

Leveling of Philosophy. Several difficulties can be brought to bear against the reasons given for this position. They argue, as we have seen, that it is not permissible to attribute an immediate philosophical content

---

[22] Kwant and van den Berk, *art. cit.* in footnote 11, pp. 15-16.
[23] Kwant and van den Berk, *ibid.*, p. 15.

to the results of the physical sciences because, by doing so, one would try to merge two entirely different worlds of thought into a single rational synthesis and this attempt is based on the *a priori* assumption of a world-in-itself. This argument would be correct only if the philosophical realm of thought were merely another realm alongside the realms of the other sciences. But that position is extremely doubtful. For, if the realm of philosophical thought were really only a realm on the same level as the other realms of thinking, then the proper object of philosophy would have to be constituted by a limiting and abstracting thematization. Hence the object of philosophy could not be being itself, as it manifest itself originally in our original being-to-the-world, but that object would be only a certain aspect of a well-defined group of worldly be-ings, as that aspect manifests itself in an abstracting and limiting attitude.

It seems to us that philosophy makes precisely the original field of presence the object of its consideration, in order to bring to light that which at first did not immediately and clearly manifest itself, viz., being itself.[24] For the primary task of philosophy is to throw light on all eidetic structures of original reality which are merely implicitly contained in our primordial experience. What is at stake here is not a purely objective side of worldly things thematized by the sciences, but the meaning of things as it manifests itself for the first time in our being-to-the-world. That which comes to light non-thematically in that primordial experience, i.e., all structures which appear only implicitly in the co-existence of original experience, phenomenological philosophy wants to thematize explicitly in order to disclose their deepest meaning. This thematization, however, does not imply any abstraction or limitation of our view. For, despite the opposition of consciousness and the world, philosophical reflection wants to study these two in their essential relationship in order to seek from there a reply to the questions concerning being, manifesting itself in this interrelationship. In this second phase philosophy asks itself what the proper mode of being is of the dis-closed structures, what the meaning is of the be-ing which, experiencing these be-ings, constitutes those structures. In this phase, therefore, the phenomenological analysis changes into an ontology, which ultimately has to ask questions about the being itself of the be-ings that appeared to it in the analyses.[25]

---

[24] Heidegger, *Sein und Zeit,* pp. 50-52 (English ed., pp. 76-77) ; Merleau-Ponty, *op. cit.,* pp. 185-196.

[25] de Waelhens, *op. cit.,* p. 391. See also Chapter Seven of this book.

Implicit Philosophy. Another difficulty can be raised against the reason for rejecting a single rational synthesis. If the categories of philosophical thought are entirely foreign to those of the sciences, then either the philosophical categories would be without any content or those of the sciences would be meaning-less. But neither one nor the other position is tenable.

In reply, we would like to make the following remarks. It seems to us that the categories of any positive science are of necessity the bearers of an implicit, and usually even unconscious, philosophy. It is the task of philosophical reflection to uncover this implicit philosophy and to provide the sciences with a correct ontology.[26] A single example may suffice to illustrate the point. The physical sciences make use of such concepts as cause, effect, goal, causality, determinism, space, time, quantity, and individuality. These concepts, on the one hand, are borne by an implicit philosophy and, on the other, demand an explicit philosophical reflection, if the physicist's thinking is to understand itself fully. But these concepts originally constitute themselves in our original contact with the world in which we live; at least, this original contact gives rise to notions from which those scientific concepts are derived. Hence it is only in reflection on our original attitude and the corresponding field of presence—which is to philosophize—that one becomes explicitly conscious of the *proper* and most original meaning of the scientific concepts.[27]

The other side, however, also must be considered. As we have seen, our original being-to-the-world is the ultimate root of all scientific activity whatsoever, and the original object of any science arises through thematization from the original field of presence. But if that is true, then this original scientific experience—and indirectly therefore also any act derived from it—still contains something of that original contact insofar as it expresses a certain aspect of the be-ings which appeared originally in that contact. While it is true that this aspect was

[26] Heidegger, *Sein und Zeit*, pp. 50-52 (English ed., pp. 76-77); Merleau-Ponty, *op. cit.*, pp. 165-166, 185-189; de Waelhens, *op. cit.*, p. 99; de Waelhens, "Sciences humaines, horizon ontologique et rencontre," *Rencontre. Contributions à une psychologie humaine dédiées au Prof. F. J. J. Buytendijk,* Utrecht, 1957, pp. 492-494, 496-497.

[27] Merleau-Ponty, *op. cit.*, pp. 194-195 and footnote one on page 194. For a development of this point with respect to the concept of space, cf. Merleau-Ponty, *Phenomenology of Perception*, pp. 243-298, and Kockelmans, "Ruimte-waarneming en ruimte volgens Merleau-Ponty," *Tijdschrift voor Philosophie,* vol. 19, pp. 372-428 (especially pp. 417-427).

artificially isolated from the others with which it was essentially connected, it is also true that in this way it could be brought to light in a much clearer and sharper fashion. Now, it must be possible to integrate this clear and sharply-defined knowledge of that aspect again into the whole which appears to us in the field of presence proper to the attitude which involves us totally. But it is precisely this total involvement itself which philosophy has as its starting point and the object of its considerations. In this sense, therefore, science can be useful to philosophy, provided the latter manages to eliminate beforehand the "disadvantages" that are of necessity attached to an abstracting thematization.

Return to the Original Field of Presence. According to phenomenology, therefore, it is possible to return from the various "worlds" of the different sciences to our original encounter with the world, to our original field of presence, because the proper field of meaning of any science is an explicitation and development of the objective side proper to this original world. Also, it is only on this level that the value and limits of those objective "worlds" can be understood.[28] However, one could ask of what possible importance could be such a return from the physicist's world to the world of everyday life. For, isn't this world of life an *"irréfléchi,"* a non-reflective world? How, then, should such a world be able to explain the proper meaning of the physicist's world? The answer would seem to lie in this that in this reductive procedure the world of everyday life is conceived not as an *irréfléchi,* but precisely as already investigated by philosophy. For only in that way does it make sense to say that philosophy is able to help the sciences to understand themselves.

Another question arising here may best be formulated in the following way. According to phenomenology, the fundamental element of any science is its thematization, for this thematization determines its object, method, terminology and language. Since all this is essential to any given science, it will be impossible to separate that science from its method and its language. What that science says, therefore, cannot be said by means of any other method or language. Whoever divorces a science from its method and language no longer speaks of that which that science spoke of but of something else.

The reply to this difficulty can be deduced from the preceding

---

[28] Merleau-Ponty, *Phenomenology of Perception,* pp. 56-57; van de Hulst and van Peursen, *op. cit.* in footnote 1, p. 46.

considerations. First of all, it should be evident that it cannot be the intention of the above-mentioned reductive procedure to express in philosophical language and through a philosophical method exactly the same as the science in question intended to express in its own language and through the use of its own method. Secondly, it is even less the intention to repeat in a clearer and more responsible way what the sciences have expressed. What the sciences teach us cannot, as such, be expressed in a different way, because the formal object of these sciences demands both this method and this particular language. But what philosophy is able to do here is to show the sciences what they are *really* speaking about, because philosophy can explain how the objective aspect, abstracted and "impoverished" by the scientific thematization, was constituted originally in our original contact with the world. And in this way philosophy supplies the foundation and the *radical* explanation of scientific knowledge.

2. The Concrete Road from Physical Science to Philosophy

Explicitation. Regarding the question of how, concretely speaking, the road from the sciences to philosophy should be conceived, it seems to us that Merleau-Ponty shows the way in this matter. He points out that the original phenomena of the everyday world of life can never be wholly unknown to scientific consciousness. For science borrows all its representations from the structures of "lived" experience, although it does not explicitly thematize this "lived" experience and does not *ex professo* explicitate the horizons of the perceptive consciousness surrounding it, the concrete relations of which it endeavors to express objectively. Accordingly, to experience those phenomena is not to search for an unknown reality, devoid of any methodic access, but to explicitate or dis-close the pre-scientific life of our consciousness, which alone is able to give full meaning to the pursuit of science and to which this pursuit always refers.

There is no question in all this of unreasonably deflecting the natural direction of our consciousness, but of an intentional analysis.[29] For, the original meaning of the intentional analysis, which the phenomenological method is *par excellence,* lies precisely in the unveiling of the implicit

---

[29] Merleau-Ponty, *ibid.,* p. 59.

potentialities pertaining to the various modes which our original being-in-the-world can assume. Generally speaking, therefore, it is a method to bring to light and explicitate meanings, to single out and discover constituent elements, which in a particular attitude toward the world were given merely implicitly, albeit actually. We have sufficiently insisted on this point in the preceding pages; hence there is no need to dwell longer on it here.[30]

Starting Point of the Intentional Analysis. The question of where such an intentional analysis can best begin has already been touched when we attempted to apply that analysis to the date of the theory of relativity. Nevertheless, it may be useful to formulate and explain our standpoint in this matter explicitly in this final chapter. The intentional analysis can *per se* be applied to any scientific act whatsoever, insofar as any intentional act can be analyzed and described in its noetic and noematic aspects. Actually, however, it seems desirable for more than one reason not to take any arbitrary scientific act as the starting point of such an analysis. First of all, the scientific vision is expressed in mathematical formulae and in a mathematical symbolism whose proper physical meaning is neither immediately clear nor univocally determined. The mathematical formalism has to be interpreted from the standpoint of the experiments from which, at least in part, it arose and in which, on the other hand, it has to find its verification with respect to the events of nature. Viewed in this fashion, the experiments appear more important than the mathematical considerations, although it is true, of course, that they would have no genuinely scientific meaning without the mathematical element. For this reason Part Two of this study applied the intentional analysis mainly to certain experiments, but those experiments were viewed in connection with the relevant theories because of the dialectic relationship between theory and experiment.

Use of Logical Analysis. In our intentional analyses we also made use of logical analysis and the results of the critique of the sciences. Although the reasons for doing so have been indicated in the Introduction, we may briefly summarize them in this concluding chapter. A logician, in the sense in which the term has been used in this book, starts from the assumption that a scientific theory is a calculus capable of interpretation. For him, the task of physical science is to construct such calculi on the basis of its observations. The logic of the sciences

---

[30] See above, Chapter Two.

takes those calculi as the object of its investigations and studies the logical aspect of the physical theories in syntactic and semantic analyses. Once the syntactic analyses have determined the formal and deductive rules governing the theory logically, they should be followed by an inquiry into the connection of such a calculus with the results of the empirical investigation, because only in this way will it be possible to see whether the theory in question is in agreement with observation and consequently also with physical reality.

We would like to point out here that the statements of a theory can only then be compared with experience and with physical reality when one has succeeded in transposing the theoretical conclusions into ordinary language according to fixed rules of interpretation and in keeping with the characteristic terminology proper to the physical system in question. The reason is that only this ordinary language is used in the description of our concrete measuring experiences.[31]   Even when this transposition is made, it should be obvious that nothing at all has yet been said concerning the nature of the physical reality in question, since that question is not a logical but an ontological problem.   On the other hand, anyone will readily admit that such a logical analysis is a very appropriate way for understanding the *physical* meaning of the theory and that it can lead us to the point where an intentional analysis can best be started.

Critique of the Sciences.   Studies in the critique of the sciences also contain many problems and ideas that can be used to advantage for an intentional analysis.   For, they speak about scientific experiences and experiments, about the meaning of scientific theories, and especially about the relationship between theory and experiment—all of which are points that appear very important for the problem studied by the phenomenologist.   Yet, certain restrictions impose themselves with respect to the consultation of such studies.

First of all, in many cases one will have to pay more attention to what such studies want to convey than to what they explicitly say.   Otherwise it will be very difficult to avoid certain *a priori's* and prejudices of positivistic or idealistic philosophy.

Secondly, the critique of the sciences always has the added intention of wanting to present the aims and results of science to a larger public than can be reached, as a rule, in professional periodicals and books.   Such

---

[31] Beth, *Natuurphilosophie*, pp. 60, 154-164.

more or less popular presentations are always interpretations of physical theories to which other physicists will very often fail to agree.

Thirdly, the critique of the sciences, especially that of our time, is interested not so much in the meaning and scope of scientific thought in its most general aspects as in the meaning of certain concrete results of scientific research.[32]

Finally, such studies are usually written by men who are, first and foremost, physicists. Because they are less familiar with philosophy, Einstein's statement applies to them: "If you wish to learn from the theoretical physicist anything about the methods he uses, I would give you the following piece of advice: Don't listen to his words, examine his achievements."[33]

Be this as it may, it appears evident that the phenomenologist can make use of such studies in the critique of the sciences only after they have been stripped of every philosophical *a priori*. The same principle, moreover, should be followed if the intentional analysis starts immediately with the professional activity of the physicist. The reason is that any statement of a positive science is made against the background of an implicit ontology, insofar as any view of a positive science must necessarily imply a fundamental vision of the world, of man, and of their original relationship.[34] An intentional analysis, therefore, can be made successfully only after a phenomenological reduction has been applied to the material serving as its starting point.

---

[32] Beth, *Inleiding tot de wijsbegeerte der exacte wetenschappen,* pp. 13-14, *Natuurphilosophie,* pp. 59-60.

[33] Einstein, *On the Method of Theoretical Physics,* Oxford, 1933, p. 163.

[34] de Waelhens, *art. cit.* in footnote 26, p. 496.

BIBLIOGRAPHY

This bibliography includes only the works mentioned in this book and other works consulted by the author.

F. Albergamo, *La critica della scienza del novecento,* Firenze, 1950.

F. Allport, *Theories of Perception and the Concept of Structure.* New York, 1955.

M. Altweg, "Theorie und Erfahrung," *Dialectica,* vol. 7 (1953), pp. 5-21.

H. Asemissen, "Strukturanalytische Probleme der Wahrnehmung in der Phänomenologie Husserls," *Kantstudien,* Erg. H. 73, Köln, 1957.

G. Bachelard, *L'activité rationaliste de la physique contemporaine,* Paris, 1951.

S. Bachelard, *La conscience de rationalité. Etude phénoménologique sur la physique mathématique,* Paris, 1958.

   La logique de Husserl. Etude sur la logique formelle et logique transcendentale, Paris, 1957.

L. Barnett, *The Universe and Dr. Einstein,* New York, 1948.

B. Bavink, *Ergebnisse und Probleme der Naturwissenschaften,* Zürich, 1959.

O. Becker, "Die Philosophie Edmund Husserls," *Kantstudien,* vol. 35 (1929), pp. 119-150.

J. Becquerel, *Le principe de la relativité et la théorie de la gravitation,* Paris, 1922.

A. Benjamin, *An Introduction to the Philosophy of Science,* New York, 1937.

G. Berger, *Le cogito dans la philosophie de Husserl,* Paris, 1941.

B. Bergmann, *Introduction to the Theory of Relativity,* New York, 1946.

E. Beth, *Inleiding tot de wijsbegeerte der exacte wetenschappen,* Amsterdam, 1953.

   Natuurfilosofie, Gorinchem, 1948.

W. Biemel, "Das Wesen der Dialektik bei Hegel und Sartre," *Tijdschrift voor Philosophie,* vol. 20 (1958), pp. 269-300.

   "Heideggers Begriff des Daseins," *Studia Catholica,* vol. 24 (1949), pp. 113-129.

   "Husserls Encyclopaedia-Britannica Artikel and Heideggers Anmerkungen dazu," *Tijdschrift voor Philosophie,* vol. 12 (1950), pp. 246-280.

Le concept du monde chez Heidegger, Paris, 1950.

I. Bocheński, *Die zeitgenössischen Denkmethoden,* München, 1954.

R. Boehm, "Zijn en tijd in de philosophie van Husserl," *Tijdschrift voor Philosophie,* vol. 21 (1959), pp. 243-276.

H. Boelaars, "De intentionaliteit der kennis bij Edmund Husserl," *Bijdragen,* vol. 3 (1940), pp. 111-116 and 221-264.

N. Bohr, *Atomic Physics and Human Knowledge,* New York, 1958.

Atomic Theory and the Description of Nature, Cambridge, 1934.

M. Born, *Atomic Physics,* London, 1946.

Experiment and Theory in Physics, London, 1944.

G. Brand, *Welt, Ich und Zeit,* Den Haag, 1955.

G. Bremer, *Wijsgerige aspecten van het natuurkundig tijdbegrip,* Utrecht, 1955.

F. Brentano, *Psychologie vom empirischen Standpunkt,* Leipzig, 1924.

S. Breton, *Approches phénoménologiques de l'idée d'être,* Paris, 1959.

Conscience et intentionnalité, Lyon, 1956.

R. Braithwaite, *Scientific Explanation,* Cambridge, 1959.

P. Bridgman, *The Logic of Modern Physics,* New York, 1927.

The Nature of Physical Theory, Princeton, 1936.

The Nature of Some of Our Physical Concepts, New York, 1952.

A. Brunner, *La personne incarnée,* Paris, 1947.

M. Buber, *Das Problem des Menschen,* Heidelberg, 1948.

F. Buytendijk, "Vernieuwing in de wetenschap," *Annalen v. h. Thijmgenootschap,* vol. 42 (1954), pp. 230-247.

R. Carnap, *Einführung in die symbolische Logik mit besonderer Berücksichtigung ihrer Anwendungen,* Wien, 1960.

"Foundations of Logic and Mathematics," *International Encyclopedia of Unified Science,* Vol. I, no. 3, Chicago, 1957.

Inductive and Deductive Logic, Chicago, 1950.

Physikalische Begriffsbildung, Karlsruhe, 1926.

The Unity of Science, London, 1934.

E. Cassirer, *Das Erkenntnisproblem in der Philosophie und Wissenschaft der neueren Zeit,* Stuttgart, 1957.

J. Clay, "Le rapport entre l'expérience et la théorie," *Dialectica,* vol. 6 (1952), pp. 266-269.

Schets ener kritische geschiedenis van het begrip natuurwet, Leiden, 1915.

O. Costa de Beauregard, *La théorie de la relativité restreinte,* Paris, 1949.

W. Dampier, *A History of Science and Its Relations with Philosophy and Religion,* Cambridge, 1948.

L. de Broglie, *Continu et discontinu en physique moderne,* Paris, 1941.
Matter and Light, New York, 1939.
Recueil d'exposé sur les ondes et corpuscules, Paris, 1930.
Sur les sentiers de la science, Paris, 1959.

B. Delfgaauw, "Heidegger en Sartre," *Tijdschrift voor Philosophie,* vol. 10 (1948), pp. 403-446.
Wat is existentialisme?, Amsterdam, 1952.

A. Dempf, *Die Einheit der Wissenschaft,* Stuttgart, 1955.

A. de Muralt, *L'idée de la phénoménologie. L'exemplarisme husserlien,* Paris, 1958.

D. De Petter, "Het tweede internationaal colloquium over de phaenomenologie. Krefeld, 1-3 november 1956," *Tijdschrift voor Philosophie,* vol. 18 (1956), pp. 724-739.

L. de Raeymaeker, W. Mund, J. Ladrière, *La relativité de notre connaissance,* Louvain, 1948.

F. Dessauer, *Naturwissenschaftliches Erkennen. Beiträge zur Naturphilosophie,* Frankfurt a.M., 1957.

J. Destouches, *Essai sur la forme générale des théories physiques,* Paris, 1938.
Physique moderne et philosophie, Paris, 1939.
Principes fondamentaux de physique théorique, Paris, 1942.

A. de Waelhens, *Chemins et impasses de l'ontologie heideggerienne. A propos des Holzwege,* Louvain, 1953.
"De taalphilosophie volgens M. Merleau-Ponty," *Tijdschrift voor Philosophie,* vol. 16 (1954), pp. 402-418.
Existence et signification, Louvain, 1958.
"Heidegger, Platon et l'humanisme," *Revue philosophique de Louvain,* vol. 46 (1948), pp. 490-496.
"Heidegger et le problème de la métaphysique," *Revue philosophique de Louvain,* vol. 52 (1954), pp. 110-119.
La philosophie de Martin Heidegger, Louvain, 1955.
"L'existentialisme de M. Sartre est-il un humanisme?" *Revue philosophique de Louvain,* vol. 44 (1946), pp. 291-300.
Phénoménologie et vérité, Paris, 1953.
"Phénoménologie husserlienne et phénoménologie hégélienne," *Revue philosophique de Louvain,* vol. 52 (1954), pp. 234-249.
"Over de betekenis van het oeuvre van M. Merleau-Ponty," *Tijdschrift voor Philosophie,* vol. 12 (1950), pp. 477-503.
"Subjectiviteit en existentie," *Tijdschrift voor Philosophie,* vol. 6 (1944), pp. 283-296.

Une philosophie de l'ambiguïté. L'existentialisme de Maurice Merleau-Ponty, Louvain, 1951.

"Zijn en Niet-zijn," *Tijdschrift voor Philosophie,* vol. 7 (1945), pp. 35-116.

A. Diemer, *Edmund Husserl. Versuch einer systematischen Darstellung seiner Phänomenologie,* Meisenheim a. Glan, 1956.

E. Dijksterhuis, *Die Mechanisierung des Weltbildes,* Berlin, 1956.

H. Dingle, *The Scientific Adventure. Essays in the History and Philosophy of Science,* New York, 1953.

H. Dingler, *Die Methode der Physik,* München, 1938.

A. Dondeyne, "Beschouwingen by het atheistisch existentialisme," *Tijdschrift voor Philosophie,* vol. 13 (1951), pp. 3-41.

Contemporary European Thought and Christian Faith, Pittsburgh, 2nd impr., 1963.

"Idealisme of realisme?" *Tijdschrift voor Philosophie,* vol. 3 (1941), pp. 607-648.

"L'historicité dans la philosophie contemporaine," *Revue philosophique de Louvain,* vol. 54 (1956), pp. 5-25 and 456-477.

"Philosophie van de tijd en metaphysica," *Tijdschrift voor Philosophie,* vol. 21 (1959), pp. 491-517.

P. Duhem, *La théorie physique. Son objet et sa structure,* Paris, 1906.

A. Eddington, *Fundamental Theory,* Cambridge, 1946.

New Pathways in Science, Cambridge, 1935.

Space, Time and Gravitation, Cambridge, 1953.

The Mathematical Theory of Relativity, Cambridge, 1954.

The Nature of the Physical World, Cambridge, 1948.

The Philosophy of Physical Science, Cambridge, 1949.

A. Einstein, *Äther und Relativitätstheorie,* Berlin, 1920.

"Die Grundlagen der allgemeinen Relativitätstheorie," *Annalen der Physik,* vol. 49 (1916), pp. 772-822.

Geometrie und Erfahrung, Berlin, 1921.

Ideas and Opinions, London, 1954.

Mein Weltbild, Amsterdam, 1934.

On the Method of Theoretical Physics, Oxford, 1933.

Relativity. The Special and General Theory, London, 1954.

The Meaning of Relativity, London, 1950.

Über die spezielle und die allgemeine Relativitätstheorie, Braunschweig, 1922.

and L. Infeld, *The Evolution of Physics,* Cambridge, 1938.

F. Engel, *Braucht der Physiker Erkenntnistheorie? Eine Gegenüberstellung von transzendentale Philosophie und Naturwissenschaft,* Halle a.d. S., 1947.

M. Farber, *Philosophical Essays in Memory of Edmund Husserl,* Cambridge, 1941.

    The Foundation of Phenomenology, Cambridge, 1943.

E. Fink, *Alles und Nichts. Ein Umweg zur Philosophie,* Den Haag, 1959.

    "Das Problem der Phänomenologie Edmund Husserls," *Revue internationale de Philosophie,* vol. 1 (1938-39), pp. 226-270.

    "Die phänomenologische Philosophie Edmund Husserls in der gegenwärtigen Kritik," *Kantstudien,* vol. 38 (1933), pp. 319-383.

    Sein, Wahrheit, Welt. Vor-Fragen zum Problem des Phänomen-Begriffs, Den Haag, 1958.

    Zur ontologischen Frühgeschichte von Raum-Zeit-Bewegung, Den Haag, 1957.

A. Fokker, *Filosofie in de natuurkunde,* Den Haag, 1949.

    "Over de absoluta der chronogeometrie," *Kon. Ned. Akad. d. Wetenschappen,* vol. 64 (1955), pp. 133-141.

    Relativiteitstheorie, Groningen, 1929.

    "Relativistische studie," *De Gids,* vol. 86 (1922), pp. 244-271.

    Tijd en ruimte, traagheid en zwaarte. Chronogeometrische inleiding tot Einstein's theorie, Zeist, 1960.

P. Fontan, "Le primat de l'acte sur l'énoncé. A propos de la 'Phénoménologie de la perception,' " *Revue philosophique de Louvain,* vol. 53 (1955), pp. 40-53.

P. Foulquié, *L'existentialisme,* Paris, 1953.

Ph. Frank, "Foundations of Physics," *International Encyclopedia of Unified Science,* Vol. 1, No. 7, Chicago, 1946.

    Philosophy of Science. The Link Between Science and Philosophy, New York, 1957.

    Validation of Scientific Theories, Boston, 1957.

    Wahrheit—Relativ oder absolut?, Zürich, 1952.

G. Frey, "Phänomenologische und operationale Begründung der Naturwissenschaften," *Kantstudien,* vol. 45 (1953-54), pp. 33-54.

S. Gagnebin, "Théorie et expérience. Le Problème," *Dialectica,* vol. 6 (1952), pp. 120-129.

W. Gerlach, E. Grassi, T. von Uexküll, G. Bally, W. Szilasi, *Die Einheit unseres Wirklichkeitsbildes und die Grenzen der Einzelwissenschaften,* München, 1951.

C. Graumann, *Grundlagen einer Phänomenologie und Psychologie der Perspektivität,* Berlin, 1960.

H. Groot, *Geheimen van ruimte en tijd,* Amsterdam, 1947.

A. Gurwitsch, "Phänomenologie der Thematik und des reinen Ich.

Studien über Beziehungen von Gestalttheorie und Phänomenologie,"
Psychologische Forschung, vol. 12 (1929), pp. 279–381.

The Field of Consciousness, Pittsburgh, 1964.

A. Hardy, *Der Begriff der Physis in der griechischen Philosophie,*
Berlin, 1884.

M. Hartmann, *Die philosophischen Grundlagen der Naturwissenschaften,* Jena, 1948.

N. Hartmann, *Grundzüge einer Metaphysik der Erkenntnis,* Berlin,
1949.

    Philosophie der Natur. Abriss der speziellen Kategorienlehre,
    Berlin, 1950.

G. Hegel, *Phänomenologie des Geistes,* ed. J. Hoffmeister, Hamburg,
1952.

M. Heidegger, *Einführung in die Metaphysik,* Tübingen, 1953; English
ed., *Introduction to Metaphysics,* New Haven, 1959; reprinted New
York, 1961.

    Holzwege, Frankfurt a.M., 1957.

    Platons Lehre von der Wahrheit. Mit einem Brief über den
    "Humanismus," Bern, 1954.

    Sein und Zeit, Tübingen, 1953; English ed., *Being and Time,*
    New York, 1962.

    Vom Wesen der Wahrheit, Frankfurt a.M., 1954; English ed., *On*
    the Essence of Truth, in Heidegger, *Existence and Being,*
    London, n.d.

    Vom Wesen und Begriff der Physis. Aristoteles Physik.B.I.
    Milano, 1960.

    Vorträge und Aufsätze, Pfullingen, 1959.

    Was heisst Denken?, Tübingen, 1954.

    Was ist Metaphysik?, Frankfurt a.M., 1955; English ed., *What is*
    Metaphysics? in Heidegger, *Existence and Being,* London,
    n.d.

W. Heisenberg, *Das Naturbild der heutigen Physik,* Hamburg, 1957.

    Wandlungen in den Grundlagen der Naturwissenschaft, Leipzig.

P. Hoenen, *Cosmologia,* Roma, 1945.

    Philosophie der anorganische natuur, Nijmegen, 1947.

G. Holton, *Introduction to Concepts and Theories in Physical Science,*
Cambridge, 1952.

R. Hooykaas, *Het begrip element in zijn historisch-wijsgerige ontwikkeling,* Utrecht, 1933.

E. Husserl, *Cartesianische Meditationen und Pariser Vorträge,* Den
Haag, 1950; English ed., *Cartesian Meditations,* Den Haag, 1960.

    Die Idee der Phänomenologie, Den Haag, 1950.

Die Krisis der europäischen Wissenschaften und die transzendentale Phänomenologie. Den Haag, 1954.

"Entwurf einer 'Vorrede' zu den 'Logischen Untersuchungen,' " 1913 published in *Tijdschrift voor Philosophie,* vol. 1 (1939), pp. 106-133 and 319-339.

Erfahrung und Urteil, ed. by L. Landgrebe, Hamburg, 1954.

Erste Philosophie (1923/24), 2 vols., Den Haag, 1956-59.

Formale und tranzendentale Logik, Halle a.d.S., 1928.

Ideen zu einer reinen Phänomenologie und phänomenologischen Philosophie, 3 vols., Den Haag, 1950-52. Volume One has been translated as *Ideas. General Introduction to Pure Phenomenology* by W. R. Boyce Gibson, Macmillan, 1931. Paperback ed., New York, 1962.

Logische Untersuchungen, 3 vols., Halle a.d.S., 1928.

"Philosophie als strenge Wissenschaft," *Logos,* 1910-11, pp. 289-341.

J. Hyppolite, *Genèse et structure de la phénoménologie de l'esprit,* 2 vols., Paris, 1946.

G. Isaye, "Expérience et théorie. Les troisièmes entretiens de Zürich," *Revue philosophique de Louvain,* vol. 49 (1951), pp. 446-461.

K. Jaspers, *Einführung in die Philosophie,* München, 1957; English ed., *Way to Wisdom. Introduction to Philosophy,* New Haven, (1951). *Philosophie,* 3 vols., Berlin, 1956.

J. Jeans, *The Growth of Physical Science,* Cambridge, 2nd ed., 1951. *Physics and Philosophy,* Cambridge, 1948. *The New Background of Science,* Cambridge, 1953.

G. Jeffery, *The Unity of Knowledge,* Cambridge, 1950.

M. Johnson, *Science and the Meaning of Truth,* London, 1946.

R. Jolivet, *L'homme métaphysique,* Paris, 1958. "Le problème de l'absolu dans la philosophie de M. Merleau-Ponty," *Tijdschrift voor Philosophie,* vol. 19 (1957), pp. 53-100.

P. Jordan, *Die Physik des 20 Jahrhunderts,* Braunschweig, 1938. *Schwerkraft und Weltall,* Braunschweig, 1955.

I. Kant, *Werke,* ed. by E. Cassirer, Berlin, 1912–22.

S. Kierkegaard, *Works,* published in English ed. under their separate titles by Princeton University Press, 1941 ff.

J. J. Kochelmans, "De betekenis van de term 'materia intelligibilis' in de werken van St. Thomas," *Tijdschrift voor Philosophie,* vol. 15 (1953), pp. 71-114. "Het standpunt van de phaenomenologie met betrekking tot de vraag over de verhouding tussen zijn en verschijnen," *Tijdschrift voor Philosophie,* vol. 22 (1960), pp. 544-587.

"Natuurwetenschap en wijsbegeerte volgens de opvatting van de phaenomenologie," *Studia Catholica,* vol. 34 (1959), pp. 28-60.

"Phaenomenologie van de waarneming volgens Aron Gurwitsch," *Tijdschrift voor Philosophie,* vol. 20 (1958), pp. 57-114.

"Realisme—idealisme en Husserls phaenomenologie," *Tijdschrift voor Philosophie,* vol. 20 (1958), pp. 395-442.

"Ruimtewaarneming en ruimte volgens Merleau-Ponty," *Tijdschrift voor Philosophie,* vol. 19 (1957), pp. 372-428.

Tijd en ruimte, Haarlem, 1958.

Martin Heidegger. A First Introduction to His Philosophy. Pittsburgh, 1965.

Edmund Husserl. Een inleiding tot zijn fenomenologie, Tielt, 1963.

Ph. Kohnstam, L. Linschoten, M. Langeveld, B. Kouwer, D. van Lennep, P. Palland, *Inleiding tot de psychologie,* Groningen, 1955.

B. Kouwer, J. Linschoten, *Inleiding tot de psychologie,* Assen, 1958.

H. Kramers, *Theorien des Aufbaues der Materie,* 2 vols., Leipzig, 1938.

A. Kuipers, *Model en inzicht,* Assen, 1959.

R. Kwant, *The Phenomenological Philosophy of Merleau-Ponty,* Pittsburgh, 1963.

"Het phenomenologich wetenschapsideaal," *Tijdschrift voor Zielkunde en Opvoedingsleer,* vol. 41 (1955), pp. 2-43.

"De geslotenheid van Merleau-Ponty's wijsbegeerte," *Tijdschrift voor Philosophie,* vol. 19 (1957), pp. 217-273.

"De historie en het absolute. Kritische analyse van de opvatting van Merleau-Ponty," *ibid.,* vol. 17 (1955), pp. 255-305.

"De mensopvatting van Maurice Merleau-Ponty," *Theologische Week,* Nijmegen, 1958.

"De zingedachte van Maurice Merleau-Ponty," *Bijdragen,* vol. 16 (1955), pp. 1-32.

and J. Van den Beek, "Het gesprek van de physicus met de wereld. Poging tot beschrijving van de physische instelling," *Annalen v.h. Thijmgenootschap,* vol. 43 (1955), pp. 1-19.

J. Lacroix, *Personne et amour,* Paris, 1955.

A. Lalande, *Vocabulaire technique et critique de la philosophie,* Paris, 1947.

L. Landgrebe, *Phänomenologie und Metaphysik,* Hamburg, 1949.

Philosophie der Gegenwart, Bonn, 1952.

"Seinsregionen und regionale Ontologien in Husserls Phänomenologie," *Studium generale,* vol. 9 (1956), pp. 313-324.

G. Laplace, *Essai philosophique des probabilités,* Paris, 1814.

K. Lasswitz, *Geschichte der Atomistik vom Mittelalter bis Newton,* 2 vols., Leipzig, 1926.

Q. Lauer, *Phénoménologie de Husserl,* Paris, 1955.

E. Lévinas, *De l'existence à l'existant,* Paris, 1947.

> *En découvrant l'existence avec Husserl et Heidegger,* Paris, 1949.
>
> *La théorie de l'intuition dans la phénoménologie de Husserl,* Paris, 1930.

R. Lindsay and H. Margenau, *Foundations of Physics,* New York, 1957.

H. Lorentz, A. Einstein, H. Minkowski, *Das Relativitätsprinzip. Eine Sammlung vom Abhandlungen,* Darmstadt, 1958.

E. Lowyck, *Substantiële verandering en hylemorphisme,* Leuven, 1948.

W. Luijpen, *Existential Phenomenology,* Pittsburgh, 5th impr., 1966.

> "Phaenomenologie van de vrijheid," *Tijdschrift voor Philosophie,* vol. 20 (1958), pp. 601-645.
>
> "Phaenomenologie van het recht," *Annalen v.h. Thijmgenootschap,* vol. 48 (1958), pp. 281-318.

A. Mansion, *Introduction à la physique aristotélicienne,* Paris, 1945.

G. Marcel, *Etre et avoir,* Paris, 1935; English ed., *Being and Having,* Westminster, (1951).

> *Journal métaphysique,* Paris, 1935; English ed., London, 1952.
>
> *L'homme problématique,* Paris, 1955.
>
> *Le mystère de l'être,* Paris, 1951; English ed., *The Mystery of Being,* 2 vols., London, 1950-51.

J. Maréchal, *Le point de départ de la métaphysique,* 5 vols., Paris, 1944-49.

H. Margenau, *The Nature of Physical Reality,* New York, 1950.

> and G. Murphy, *The Mathematics of Physics and Chemistry,* New York, 1953.

A. Mariétan, *Problème de la classification des sciences,* Paris, 1901.

M. Merleau-Ponty, *Eloge de la philosophie,* Paris, 1953; English ed., *In Praise of Philosophy,* Evanston, Ill., 1963.

> *La structure du comportement,* Paris, 1949; English ed., Boston, 1963.
>
> *Phénoménologie de la perception,* Paris, 1945; English ed., New York, 1962.
>
> *Sens et Non-Sens,* Paris, 1948; English ed., Evanston, 1964.

E. Meyerson, *Identité et réalité,* Paris, 1951.

> *La déduction relativiste,* Paris, 1925.

C. Møller, *The Theory of Relativity,* Oxford, 1952.

E. Mounier, *Introduction aux existentialismes,* Paris, 1947; English ed., *Existentialist Philosophies,* London, 1948.

E. Nickel, *Das "physikalische Modell" und die "metaphysische Wirklichkeit." Versuch einer Metaphänomenologie,* München, 1952.

J. Nota, "Phaenomenologie als methode," *Tijdschrift voor Philosophie,* vol. 3 (1941), pp. 203-240.

D. Nys, *La notion d'espace,* Louvain, 1930.

G. Pedroli, *La fenomenologia di Husserl,* Torino, 1958.

M. Planck, *Wege zur physikalischen Erkenntnis,* Leipzig, 1943.

H. Poincaré, *La valeur de la science,* Paris, 1912.
   Science and Hypothesis, New York, 1952.

H. Pos, *Filosofie der wetenschappen,* Arnhem, 1953.

H. Reichenbach, *Philosophie der Raum-Zeit-Lehre,* Berlin, 1928.

F. Renoirte, *Cosmology,* New York, 1950.
   "La critique einsteinienne des mesures d'espace et de temps," *Revue néo-scolastique de philosophie,* vol. 26 (1924), pp. 267-298.
   "La théorie physique. Introduction à l'étude d'Einstein," *Revue néoscolastique de philosophie,* vol. 25 (1923), pp. 349-375.

H. Rickert, *Die Grenzen der naturwissenschaftlichen Begriffsbildung,* Tübingen, 1921.

P. Ricoeur, "Etude sur les 'Méditations Cartésiennes' de Husserl," *Revue philosophique de Louvain,* vol. 52 (1954), pp. 75-109.
   "Husserl et le sens de l'histoire," *Revue de métaphysique et de morale,* vol. 54 (1949), pp. 280-316.
   Idées directrices pour une phénoménologie, Paris, 1950.

A. Robb, *Geometry of Space and Time,* Cambridge, 1936.
   The Absolute Relations of Space and Time, Cambridge, 1921.

J. Robert, "Eléments de bibliographie husserlienne," *Tijdschrift voor Philosophie,* vol. 20 (1958), pp. 534-544.

J. Rossell, "Théorie et expérience," *Dialectica,* vol. 6 (1952), pp. 260-263.

A. Rubin, *Visuell wahrgenommene Figuren,* København, 1921.

J.-P. Sartre, "La transcendance de l'ego," *Recherches philosophiques,* vol. 6 (1936-37), pp. 85-123.
   L'être et le néant, Paris, 1948; English ed., *Being and Nothingness,* New York, 1956.
   L'existentialisme est un humanisme, Paris, 1954; English ed., *Existentialism and Humanism,* London, 3rd impr., 1951.

F. Sassen and B. Delfgaauw, *Wijsbegeerte van onze tijd,* Antwerpen, 1957.

M. Scheler, *Abhandlungen und Aufsätze,* Berlin, 1925.
   Bildung und Wissen, Frankfurt a.M., 1947.

E. Schrödinger, *Die Natur und die Griechen,* Hamburg, 1956.
   Space-Time Structure, Cambridge, 1953.

L. Schuwer, "De zijnsleer van Martin Heidegger," *Studia Catholica,* vol. 26 (1951), pp. 78-87.

J. Seiler, *Philosophie der unbelebten Natur,* Olten, 1948.

F. Selvaggi, "Assoluto e relativo nel tempo," *Gregorianum,* vol. 28 (1947), pp. 337-356.

    Filosofia delle scienze, Roma, 1953.

    "Il significato della relatività," *Gregorianum,* vol. 33 (1952), pp. 418-437.

S. Strasser, "Beschouwingen over het vraagstuk der apodicticiteit en de critische verantwoording van de phaenomenologie," *Tijdschrift voor Philosophie,* vol. 8 (1946), pp. 226-270.

    "Het vraagstuk van het solipsisme bij Edmund Husserl," *Tijdschrift voor Philosophie,* vol. 7 (1945), pp. 3–18.

    "Het wezen van de mens," *Annalen v.h. Thijmgenootschap,* vol. 46 (1958), pp. 1-32.

    The Soul in Metaphysical and Empirical Psychology, Pittsburgh, 2nd impr., 1962.

    Phenomenology and Human Science, Pittsburgh, 1963.

B. Swanenburg, *De verovering der materie. De groei van het wereldbeeld der natuurkunde van de Grieken tot heden,* Utrecht, 1950.

J. Synge, *Relativity: The Special Theory,* Amsterdam, 1956.

H. Tornebohm, *A Logical Analysis of the Theory of Relativity,* Stockholm, 1952.

S. Toulman, *The Philosophy of Science,* London, 1955.

H. Van Breda, "Het 'zuivere phaenomeen' volgens Edmund Husserl," *Tijdschrift voor Philosophie,* vol. 3 (1941), pp. 447-498.

H. van de Hulst and C. van Peursen, *Phaenomenologie en natuurwetenschap,* Utrecht, 1953.

L. Van Haecht, "Phaenomenologische analyse van het menselijk lichaam naar Edmund Husserl," *Tijdschrift voor Philosophie,* vol. 6 (1944), pp. 135-190.

A. van Melsen, *De wijsbegeerte der exacte wetenschappen,* Groningen, 1954.

    Het wijsgerig verleden der atoomtheorieën, Amsterdam, 1941.

    From Atomos to Atom. The History of the Concept "Atom," Pittsburgh, 1952.

    The Philosophy of Nature, Pittsburgh, 4th impr., 1961.

    Science and Technology, Pittsburgh, 1962.

C. van Peursen, *Lichaam, ziel, geest,* Utrecht, 1956.

    Riskante filosifie. Een karakteristiek van het hedendaagse existentiële denken, Amsterdam, 1955.

C. Verhoeven, "De betekenis van het woord 'existere,'" *Studia Catholica,* vol. 32 (1957), pp. 1-28.

T. von Uexküll and E. Grassi, *Wirklichkeit als Geheimnis und Auftrag. Die Exaktheit der Naturwissenschaften und die philosophische Erfahrung,* Bern, 1945.

C. von Weizsäcker and J. Juilfs, *Physik der Gegenwart,* Bonn, 1953.

J. Wahl, *Etudes kierkegaardiennes,* Paris, 1949.

W. Watson, *On Understanding Physics,* Cambridge, 1938.

B. Welte, "Remarques sur l'ontologie de Heidegger," *Revue des sciences philosophiques et théologiques,* vol. 31 (1947), pp. 379-393.

A. Wenzl, *Die philosophischen Grenzfragen der modernen Naturwissenschaft,* Stuttgart, 1954.

H. Weyl, *Philosophy of Mathematics and Natural Science,* Princeton, 1949.

   Raum-Zeit-Materie, Berlin, 1920.

   "Wissenschaft als symbolische Konstruktion des Menschen," *Eranos Jahrbuch,* vol. 16 (1948), pp. 375-431.

N. Wiener, *Cybernetics,* New York, 1953.

A. Whitehead, *Process and Reality,* Cambridge, 1929.

E. Whittaker, *A History of the Theories of Aether and Electricity. The Modern Theories, 1900-1926,* London, 1953.

   From Euclid to Eddington. A Study of the Conceptions of the External World, Cambridge,1949.

   Space and Spirit, London, 1952.

J. Witt-Hansen, *Exposition and Critique of the Conceptions of Eddington Concerning the Philosophy of Physical Science,* Copenhagen, 1958.

J. Yolton, *The Philosophy of Science of A. S. Eddington,* Den Haag, 1960.

COLLECTIVE TITLES

Albert Einstein: Philosopher-Scientist, ed. by P. Schilpp, New York, 2nd ed., 1951.

Fünfzig Jahre Relativitätstheorie, Basel, 1956.

Husserl et la pensée moderne. Actes du 2e colloque international de phénoménologie. Krefeld 1–3 novembre 1956; ed. by H. Van Breda and J. Taminiaux, Den Haag, 1959.

Husserl. Actes du 3e colloque international de phénoménologie; Cahiers de Royaumont, Philosophie, no. III, ed. by M. A. Bera, Paris, 1959.

Truth and Freedom by Louis de Raeymaeker and other professors of the University of Louvain, Pittsburgh, 1954.

Liberté. Actes du 4e Congrès des sociétés de philosophie de langue française, Neuchâtel, 1949.

Phénoménologie—Existence. Recueil d'études par H. Birault, H. Van Breda, A. Gurwitsch, E. Lévinas, P. Ricoeur, et J. Wahl, Paris, 1953.

Problèmes actuels de la phénoménologie. Actes du colloque interna-

tional de phénoménologie, Bruxelles, avril 1951, ed. by H. Van Breda, Brugge, 1952.

Readings in the Philosophy of Science, ed. by H. Feigl and M. Broderick, New York, 1953.

Rencontre. Contributions à une psychologie humaine dédiées au Prof. F.J.J. Buytendijk, Utrecht, 1957.

Theoretical Physics in the Twentieth Century. A Memorial Volume to Wolfgang Pauli, ed. by F. Fierz and V. Weisskopf, New York, 1960.

INDEX OF NAMES

(A small letter *n* after a number indicates that the reference is to a footnote on the page in question.)

Albergamo F., 99*n*
Alembert J. d', 71
Aristoteles, 36, 49, 70, 74, 107*n*, 157, 158, 172, 173
Augustine St., 70

Bacon Fr., 71, 73
Bavink B., 103, 104
Bergmann, B., 129*n*
Beth E., 154
Bohr N., 161
Born M., 129*n*
Brentano Fr., 36
Bridgman P., 23, 113, 114, 116, 136*n*, 139*n*
Broglie L. de, 161
Buytendijk F., 29

Carnap R., 113, 114, 116, 117, 120, 139
Cassirer E., 99*n*
Cicero C., 70
Comte A., 71, 98

Democritus, 74
Descartes, R., 18, 30, 31, 40, 71, 73, 74, 80, 81, 82
Diderot D., 71
Dirac P., 161
Dondeyne A., 29, 51

Eddington Sir A., 99, 100, 100*n*, 102, 110, 129*n*, 131*n*
Einstein A., 98, 99, 100, 101, 102, 103, 108, 109, 110, 114, 120, 123, 127, 128, 129, 129*n*, 130, 132, 133, 134*n*, 136*n*, 138, 140, 147, 154, 161, 184
Epicurians, 70
Euler L., 108

Faraday M., 105
Fichte J. G., 30, 71
FitzGerald G., 103, 108, 128, 129*n*
Fokker A., 99, 102, 110, 129*n*, 143, 144, 145, 146, 150*n*
Fresnel A., 105
Friedman A., 129*n*

Galileo Galilei, 104, 106, 107, 108, 124, 137.

Hardy E., 157
Hartmann N., 98*n*
Hassenstein P., 74
Hegel G.F.W., 16, 30, 31, 71
Heidegger M., 29, 31, 36, 39, 40, 51, 52, 56, 61, 67, 68, 88, 158, 172, 174
Heisenberg W., 80, 161
Helmholz H. von, 76
Herbart J., 76
Hertz H., 105
Hlavaty G., 129*n*
Husserl E., 18, 29, 30, 31, 32, 33, 34, 35, 36, 37, 38, 39, 40, 51, 53, 61, 72, 73, 96, 152, 165
Huygens C., 108

Jaspers K., 56, 66, 67
Jeans J., 102, 110
Jonsson T., 129*n*
Jordan P., 110, 129*n*

Kaluza Th. von, 129*n*
Kant I., 30, 48, 71, 107*n*
Keppler J., 74
Kierkegaard S., 56
Klein F., 129*n*

Kohler R., 129n
Kwant R., 29

Larmor Sir J., 103, 108, 129n
Leibniz G.W., 71
Lemaître G., 129n
Levi-Civita T., 129n
Lorentz H., 103, 108, 109, 128,
    128n, 129n, 132, 138, 154
Luijpen W., 29

Mach E., 98, 108
Mansion A., 157
Marcel G., 67
Margenau H., 114
Marx K., 71
Maxwell J., 22, 104, 105, 106,
    127
Merleau-Ponty M., 29, 31, 36,
    46, 52, 55, 58, 61, 67, 181
Meyerson E., 98, 99, 99n
Michelson A., 107, 108, 109, 127,
    128
Minkowski H., 109, 113, 129n,
    130
Minnaert M., 100
Morley F., 107, 108, 127, 128

Newton Sir I., 22, 23, 102, 104,
    105, 106, 107, 107n, 108, 109,
    122, 123, 124, 126, 139, 140,
    154

Oersted P., 105

Pavlov I., 77
Planck M., 161

Plato, 49, 70, 157
Poincaré H., 108, 121, 122, 123,
    129n
Pre-Socratics, 157, 159

Renoirte F., 98, 110
Renouvier Ch., 73
Ricci G., 129n
Ricoeur P., 40
Ritz W., 128n, 129n
Robb A., 100, 134n
Rubin A., 46
Ruggiero G. de, 99n

Sartre J.-P., 61
Scheler M., 48
Schelling F.W., 30
Schouten J., 129n
Schrödinger E., 129n, 161
Selvaggi F., 99n
Sitter W. de, 102, 129n
Stoics, 70
Synge J., 110

Thales, 157
Thorndike E., 77

Veblen O., 129n
Voigt W., 129n

Waelhens A. de, 29, 90, 165
Watson J., 77
Weizsäcker C. von, 79
Weyl H., 99, 99n, 102, 129n
Whittaker Sir E., 108, 129n
Wolff Chr. von, 79
Wundt W., 77.

INDEX OF SUBJECT MATTER

Absolute Interval, 109, 112; as absolute relation, 140-143; no fundamental concept, 143n.

Absolute Length, 108.

Absolute Motion, 108.

Absolute Relations, 99, 101, 109, 110, 111-112, 140-143, 153; meaning of these relations explained by 'geometrical' examples, 143-150.

Absolute Space and Time, 108, 124-127, 139-143, 154; critique of Einstein, 108-109, 128-129, 132, 133-134, 139-143, 154-155; relativity of measurements of space dimensions, 109, 130-133; relativity of simultaneity-at-a-distance, 109, 133-134.

Absolute Velocity, 147.

Abstract Character, of Physical Nature, 89, 151-152.

Abstraction, in Physics, 170, 177-181.

Act-Intentionality, see Intentionality.

Aition (=Cause), 172.

Analytic of Dasein, 50-51; and fundamental ontology, 51.

Anticipations, 43, 44, 46.

Apodicticity, and original intuition, 34-35.

Associationism (in psychology), 76-77

Authenticity, of man, 68; of philosophy, 16, 17.

Axiom, 20, 21, 22.

Being, mystery of, 16; the question concerning the meaning of, 49-51; of be-ings, 50-51; and man, 48-49; and philosophy, 48-49; and becoming (=coming-to-be), 157.

Being-able-to-be, 68.

Being-in-situation, 66-67.

Being-in-the-world, 13-14, 40; and ex-sistence, 52, 55; as presence and the field of presence, 61-62; as lumen naturale, 173.

Being-to-the-world, see Being-in-the-world.

Bestand (=being constantly in supply), and technology, 174; and thematized object, 174-175.

Body (human), as object and as subject, 57-58.

Bracketing of being, 36.

Categories (physical and philosophical), 177-181.

Cause, 172-173; and truth as unconcealedness, 172.

Chronogeometry, and theory of relativity, 99, 150.

Classical Physics, crisis of, 103-108; see also Physics.

Clock (ideal), 136.

Co-existence, 53-54.

Cogito, in Descartes and in Husserl's phenomenology, 40-41.

Concern (=Besorgen), 88, 166, 174.

Consciousness, as pure interiority, 39; as openness, 39; as ex-sistence, 39-40; and world, 82-83, 178.

Constitution, 39, 41, 43-44, 47; see also Intentionality and Intentional Analysis.

Contraction Theory (of Lorentz), 108, 128, 132.

Counting, 115; as absolute operation, 130.

Critique of the Sciences, as philosophy of science, 73, 96, 183-184.

Dasein, 50-51.

Deductive Theory, and physical reality, 19-20.

Definition of Physical Magnitudes, according to Carnap, 113; and Bridgman, 113-114; and Margenau, 114.

Demarcation of Field of Investigation, and thematization, 87-90; *see also* Thematization.

Destruction (=destructive retrieve), 14, 15.

Determinism, in psychology, 77.

Dialectic Relationship, between contemporary philosophy and and the philosophies of the past, 17; between man and world, 62-63; between physicist and physical world, 163-164.

Dialogue (=ex-sistence), 52.

Dis-close, as bringing into unconcealedness, 173-175.

Division of the Sciences, 70-72.

Dwelling-in-the-world, 61.

Eccentricity, and interiority, 60.

Eidetic Reduction, *see* Reduction.

Eidos, in Husserl's phenomenology, 36; and eidetic reduction, 35-36.

Electromagnetic Field, 105-106.

Elementarism, in psychology, 52.

Encounter (=ex-sistence), 52.

Enduring Straight Line, 143, 147, 148, 149.

Essence, in Husserl's phenomenology, 35.

Ether Theories, 102, 104-105, 127.

Events (spatio-temporal), 109, 112, 139; and world-events, 154-155.

'Events neither before nor after' (Robb), 134, 134*n*.

Existence, *see* Ex-sistence.

Existentialism, *see* Existential Phenomenology.

Existential Phenomenology, 19, 51-52, 53-54; and logic, 18-19; and view of man, 85-86.

Experiment, 19-20, 22-23; in physics, 168-169; *see also* Theory and Experiment.

Experiment of Michelson and Morley, 107; and interpretation by Lorentz, 108; by Einstein, 128-130.

Explanation, 89, 176; radical, 181.

Explicitation, 181-182; and intentional analysis, 181-182; as disclosing of inner horizon, 181; as un-veiling of implicit intentionalities, 181-182.

Ex-sistence, 13-15; and intentionality, 52-53; and transcendence, 52; and being-in-the-world, 52, 55; and *Dasein,* 52-53; and co-existence, 58-59; as the essence of man as being-in-the-world, 55-56; as being-open-to, 51-52; as radical intentionality, 61-62; as primitive fact in existential phenomenology, 51, 53-54; as original experience, 176.

External Horizon, 44-45.

Facticity, 13; and freedom, 66-69.

Field of Original Experience, 34.

Field of Presence, and life-world, 52, 61; as the field of meaning constituted by our primordial experience, 85; and the different fields of meaning constituted by the sciences, 84-85.

Figure-Horizon Structure, 45-46.

Finiteness of Man, 60.

Formal Calculus, 20.

Four-Dimensional Continuum, 109, 139-143.

Freedom, 13, 62, 65-69; negative aspect of, 65; positive aspect of, 65-66; and project, 65-68; situated freedom, 66-67.

Fulfillment (=*Erfüllung*), 43-44, 46.

Functioning Intentionality, and ex-sistence, 53, 61; as the root of all meaning, 61, 63-64; *see also* Intentionality.

Fundamental Ontology, 51.

Galileo-transformation, 107.

Generalities, empirical and pure, 35.

Having-to-be, 68.

Here-Now-Radii, 146-149.

Historicity, of philosophy, 15-17.

History, of Philosophy, 15-17.

Hypothesis, and deductive theory, 19.

Hypothesis of Equivalence (in classical physics), 132*n*.

Idea, in Husserl's phenomenology, 35.

Inertial Systems, 106-108.

Instrumental Causality, 172-173.

Intentional Analysis, 37, 40-47; as phenomenological method *par excellence,* 19; and constitution, 41, 47; and semantic analysis, 47; and reflection, 90-91; and philosophy of science, 96-97; of scientific theories, 181-182; and logical analysis, 182-183; and critique of the sciences, 182-184.

Intentional Correlate, of physical science, 176-177; its ontological status, 177.

Intentionality, 13-14, 18-19; of a determinate act (*Aktintentionalität*), 18, 39, 61; functioning intentionality (*fungierende Intentionalität*), 18, 39; as central intuition of existential phenomenology, 19; and constitution, 36-39; and being-in-the-world as ex-sistence, 48, 52-53, 163-166; as source of all meaning, 38-39, 62-64, 87.

Interiority, and intentionality, 59-60; as attempt of interiorization, 60.

Internal Horizon, 44, 45, 46.

Interval, *see* Absolute Interval.

Intuition (Primordial), 17, 34; as ultimate foundation of philosophy, 34-35; and apodictic evidence, 34; and *eidos,* 36.

Invariant, 35.

Isochronism, 120-129; the problem, 120-121; according to classical physics, 121-125; implications of this view, 123-125; critique of this view, 125, 129.

Knowledge, as encounter between man and world, 84; as source of a field of meaning, 84; as dialogue between man and world, 84; as a special and derivative mode of our being-in-the-world, 64, 87.

Language, of Science (and thematization), 87-88, 169, 180-181; *see also* Thematization.

Laws, 22-23, 108, 109, 167-168.

Length, *see* Absolute Length.

Life-world, as original world of our immediate experience, 61; as the one world of our original intentionality, 90-91; and the different worlds of the sciences, 90, 176-184.

Lived Experience, 37.

Logic of Physical Science, and existential phenomenology, 18-19, 19-26, 96, 182-183.

Logical Analysis, 20.

Logico-Mathematical Basic Calculus, and formal Calculus, 20; and physical Calculus, 20-23.

Lorentz-transformation, 108, 128, 138.

Magnitudes, *see* Physical Magnitudes.

Margin, and thematic field, 45.

Materialism, and view of man, 55-56.

Mathematics, and physical science, 168-169.

Meaning, its genesis and root, 38-39, 62-63, 87; as direction of our original intentions, 63; and man's ex-sistence, 62-63; and world, 63.

Measurement (in physics), 114-116, 120-121, 130-131.

Measuring, and the thematizing project of the physicist, 167-169.

Measuring Rod, 135.

Method, and thematization, 87-88; in physical science, 167-169.

Metric Numbers, 115-119; as invariable numbers, 130; relative numbers, 138; absolute numbers, 138-143.

Metric Rules, and the definition of physical quantities, 117-119.

Model, 169.

Motion, *see* Absolute Motion.

Natural Attitude, and philosophical attitude, 32-42.

Naturalism, and phenomenology, 33, 81-85, 163, 177-178.

Nature, as intentional correlate of physical science, 95, 151-153; as intentional correlate of the theory of relativity, 153-157; as the layer of spatio-temporal materiality, 152.

Noema, 42-43, 44, 45, 46, 47.

Noematic Core (=Nucelus), 44.

Noematic Reflection, 47; *see* Intentional Analysis.

Noematic System, 43.

Noesis, 42-43; 46.

Noetico-noematic Analysis, *see* Intentional Analysis.

Noetico-noematic Description, 41, 47.

Objectivation (in Science), 86-91.

Observable Properties, 20, 112, 115.

Observation, 19-20, 22-23

Obviousness, 14-15.

Openness, 13, 15; *see* Ex-sistence.

Operational Definition, and Semantic rules, 23-25.

Operational Meaning of a Scientific Term, 23.

Operational Method, according to Bridgman, 113-116; and the theory of relativity, 111-112, 129, 139-140; and hypotheses, 129n.

Original Praxis, 165-166.

Perception, analysis of an act of, 41-47.

Phenomenological Reduction, *see* Reduction.

Phenomenology, as method, 18, 29; as philosophy, 29; and Hegel, 30; and Husserl, 30-40; and 'philosophy as rigorous science' 31-32; as method of the analytic of *Dasein*, 50-51; and science, 82-85.

Philosophical Attitude, and natural attitude, 32-34.

Philosophy, and pre-philosophical thinking, 14-15; and history of philosophy, 15-17; task of, 48; and science, 90-91; as phenomenological reflection and ontology, 91; its thematization, 178; its thematizing project is neither limiting nor abstracting, 178; its subject-matter is our primordial field of presence, 178-180; its aim is the understanding of being, 178; comprises a phenomenological analytic of *Dasein* and an ontology, 178; as implicit in scientific theories, 179-180, 184.

Philosophy of Science, *see* Critique of the Sciences.

Physical Calculus, and formal calculus, 20-21; and semantic rules, 21; and logico-mathematical basic calculus, 21; and fundamental equations, 22.

Physicalization, 72, 81.

Physical Magnitudes, definition of, 113-114; and observable properties, 112-113

Physical Nature, and 'real world', 151-153; *see also* Nature.

Physical Reality (world-events, particles, bodies, spatio-temporal relations), as constituted by physics, 156; as objectified entitities, 156-157.

Physical Science, and philosophy, 160-184; studies the objective dimension of the world of our immediate experience, 176-177; constitution of its objects, 176-177, 181; its thematization, 167-169, 176, 180-181; its implicit ontology, 179-180, 184.

Physical System, 112, 115.

Physics, classical vs. contemporary, 95; as a derivative mode of man's fundamental intentionality (=being-in-the-world), 163-164; as theory of reality, 164; as theory of the objective dimension of reality, 165-167; and technology, 170-175; *see also* Physical Science.

Physis (=Nature), and the Pre-Socratics, 157; in Plato and Aristotle, 157-158.

Point-Event, 139, 153-154; as ultimate element of space-time, 154-155; as mathematical schematization of physical events, 154.

Positivism, 7; and phenomenology, 33, 81-85, 163.

Possibility-of-situations, and man, 14.

Potentiality-for-being (*Sein-können*), 13.

Praxis, *see* Original Praxis.

Pre-Ontological Understanding of Being, 50.

Pre-Philosophic Life, 14-15.

Pre-Predicative Truth, 173.

Presence (*Anwesenheit*), 52; and field of presence, 84-85; in physics, 176-177.

Presence-at-hand (*Vorhandenheit*), 88-89, 166.

Presuppositionlessness, of philosophy, 34, 48, 85.

Primordial Understanding, 14-15.

Principle of Relativity, in classical physics, 103-104, 106-107, 124-125.

Privileged System of Reference, 124, 129.

Profiles (=*Abschattungen*), 41-43, 45.

Project, 14; and being-in-the-world, 61; and freedom, 67-69; as leeway of man's factical being-able-to-be, 68-69; and transcendence, 68; and thematization, 87-88; and thematization of physical science, 165-166; objectifying project in physical science, 174-175; and producing which makes things appear as *Bestand* in technology, 174-175.

Proper-Length, 131-133, 135; of moving system, 132-133, 135-136.

Proper-Time, 136.

Property, *see* Observable Property.

Psychology, and scientism, 76-78;

and associationism, 76-77; and elementarism, 77; and determinism, 77; psychology without a soul, 77-78; objectifying psychology, 78; and the crisis of scientism, 79.

Quantum Mechanics, 25.

Radicalism, in philosophy, 34, 48, 85-86.
Rationalism, and phenomenology, 81-85, 163.
Readiness-to-hand (=*Zuhandenheit*), 88, 166.
Reality, 164; as encounter, 165; as co-existence of man and world, 165; *see also* Physical Reality.
Reduction (phenomenological), 15, 41; different forms of reduction, 34-35; eidetic reduction, 35-36; phenomenological reduction, 36-37; transcendental 36; reduction from our cultural world to the life-world, 36-38, from the worlds of the sciences to the life-world, 90-91, 180-181; and existential phenomenology, 61, 90-91, 165, 180-181.
Region of the Physical, 167-168; as the realm of the measurable, 167.
Regularity, 168.
Relativity, of space and time, 128-138.
Representationism, as the root of scientism, 81-82; and phenomenology, 82-85.
Rules of Definition, 20.
Rules of Inference, 20-21.

Science, belongs to the natural attitude, 33; is not presuppositionless, 86; is not radical, 85-86; and the essence of the domain constituting its subject matter, 86; one-sidedness of science, 86; its object is an objectified entity, 86-87; and philosophy, 176-184.
Scientism, 37-38; its roots, 72-73; characteristics of, 73-76; and philosophy, 73; and primary and secondary qualities, 74-75; and principle of determinism, 75; and unity of science, 76; in psychology, 76-78; and phenomenology, 81-85; crisis of scientism in biology, 78-79; in psychology, 79; in physical science, 79-80; root of this crisis, 80-81.
Semantic Analysis, 19; and syntactic analysis, 20-22, 183; and formal calculus, 21; and philosophical foundation, 25-26.
Semantic Rules, and operational definition, 23-25.
Semantic System (of a theory), 21-23.
Simultaneity, ambiguity of the term, 100-101; according to classical physics, 126-128; according to the theory of relativity, 133-138.
Situation, 13, 14, 15, 16, 17; and freedom, 66-67.
Space, *see* Absolute Space and Time.
Space-Time, 139, 153-155; as spatio-temporal frame of reference, 154-155.
Spatial Distance (in XT-diagram), 145.
Spiritualism, and view of man, 55.
State (of a physical system), 112.
Statistical Method, 115.
Subjectivity, and ex-sistence, 59-60.
Subject-Object Opposition, and intentionality, 62-64; in con-

temporary physics, 79-80; and the uncertainty relations, 80.

Syntactic Analysis, 20-22; 183.

Synchronism, 120-129; the problem, 120-121; according to classical physics, 125-128; implications of this view, 126-127; critique of this view, 127-129.

Technology, 170-171; essence of, 173-175; instrumental and anthropological description of, 172; as a mode of bringing into unconcealedness (=alētheia), 173-174; and truth, 171-174; and physical science, 174-175.

Telethigma, 146.

Temporal Duration (in *XT*-diagram), 145, 148.

Temporality, as essential characteristic of nature, 156-157.

Thema, 45.

Thematic Field, 45-46.

Thematization, and demarcation of field of investigation, 87-88; and method, 87-88; and truth, 87-88; and language, 87-88; and constitution, 87-88; and project, 87-88; and abstraction, 88-89; plurality of thematizations and the plurality of the sciences, 89-90; and physical science, 166-181; and philosophy, 90-91, 178.
(Of the physicist:) 166-170, 180-181; and the demarcation of the physical field of meaning, 166-167; and method, 167-169, 180-181; and truth and certainty, 169-170, 180; and language, 169, 180-181; and the thematizing project, 167-168; and the constitution of physical entities, 168.

Theorem, 20-22.

Theory, 164; and original praxis,

165-166; as a calculus capable of interpretation, 182; and logical analysis, 182-183; and phenomenological analysis, 183; and experiment, 182; and the crisis of scientism, 80.

Theory of Relativity, 24-25; the term is ambiguous, 98-99; and 'theory of invariants', 99*n;* and 'theory of absolute relations', 99; and 'chronogeometry', 99; often misunderstood by philosophers, 98; reasons of this misunderstanding, 98-103; and classical physics, 102-103; general theory of relativity, 112, 114; special theory of relativity, 108-109, 110-114.

Theory of Science, 70-72; according to phenomenology, 85-91.

Thrownness, 60, 68-69.

Time, *see* Absolute Space and Time.

Time-dilatation, 108, 128.

Time-tracks, 148.

Topological Rules, and the definition of physical quantities, 116-119.

Tradition (and philosophy), 15-17.

Transcendence, in Husserl, 38; in Heidegger and Merleau-Ponty, 60, 64-65, 67; and freedom, 67.

Transcendental Reduction, *see* Reduction.

Transcendental Sphere, as field of original experience, 35.

Transcendental Subjectivity, 36.

Truth, as Unconcealedness (*a-lētheia*), 172-174; predicative and pre-predicative truth, 173; and technology, 173-174; and philosophy, 48; logical and physical truth, 21, 23; and thematization 87-88; of physical statements, 169-170, 180.

Uncertainty Relations, and the crisis of scientism, 80.
Unconcealedness (*a-lētheia*), as truth, 172-173.
Uniform Periodic Motion, definition in classical physics, 121-123; implications of this definition, 123-125.
Unity of Science, 71-72; 81-82; 84-85.

Verification, 22, 169.

World, and consciousness, 82-83; and with-world, 58; world of immediate experience as *irréflichi,* 180; plurality of worlds, 83-84; the world of our immediate experience and the worlds of the sciences, 180.
World of the physicist, and the world of our immediate experience, 163-164; as derivative field of presence corresponding to a derivative mode of our being-in-the-world, 163-164; as objective world, 164-165; as abstract world, 165.
World-Condition, not relative, 138*n.*
World-event, 153-155.
World-Experiencing Life (*Welterfahrendes Leben*), and ex-sistence, 53.